S0-BCN-615

Nathan Sternfeld

# REBBE MENDEL

## ...in a **CLASS** by Himself

FELDHEIM PUBLISHERS
JERUSALEM · NEW YORK

Some of the stories that appear in this book originally appeared in
Hebrew in Rebbe Mendel's book, *Esrim Tze'adim* (5766)

Illustrated by David Bichman
Translated into English by S. Wolfsohn
Edited by Deena Nataf
Typeset by Eden Chachamtzedek

Also by the author:
*Adventures with Rebbe Mendel* (Jerusalem: Feldheim Publishers, 2002)
*All About Motti and His Adventures with Rebbe Mendel* (Jerusalem: Feldheim
Publishers, 2004)
*The Secret of the Red Pearl* (Jerusalem: Feldheim Publishers, 2005)
*A Home on the Hill* (Jerusalem: Feldheim Publishers, 2006)

ISBN  978-1-59826-320-6

First published 2009
Copyright © 2009 by the author

FELDHEIM PUBLISHERS
POB 43163 / Jerusalem, Israel

208 Airport Executive Park
Nanuet, NY 10954

www.feldheim.com

10  9  8  7  6  5  4  3  2  1

*Printed in Israel*

# CONTENTS

## Section 1: Life Lessons

## Section 2: Changing Perspectives

## Section 3: Laugh Lessons

# Section 4: Cast Your Bread...

Section 1

LIFE LESSONS

# CHAPTER 1

## *TWENTY PACES*

**"T**he story I am about to tell you," said Rebbe Mendel, "I heard from Rav Shmayah Katz, *z"l*, the father of my rosh yeshiva. I don't remember whether he told it about Rabbi Meir of Rothenburg — who is called the Maharam — or about Rabbeinu Meshulam. Either way, the events took place hundreds of years ago.

"This story is about a very unique act of *kiddush Hashem.* Now, before I begin, I must warn you not to draw any conclusions regarding how you are supposed to act. This is only a story. However, may it be Hashem's will that none of us ever fall into a trial such as the one I am about to describe."

*Two bachurim — whom we will call Levi and Yehudah because we don't know their real names — were the pride of their town. The two were always found in the beis midrash, studying Torah day and night.*

*After they had filled their neshamos with the study of the entire Shas, which in those days was not printed…*

"One minute," asked Moishie, "if the Shas wasn't printed, then how did they learn it?"

"They learned part of the Shas from carefully copied manuscripts — of which there were not many, since very few people

1

could afford them," answered Rebbe Mendel, "and the rest they learned orally from their rabbis, which they then wrote out for themselves, each one according to what he had heard. Whenever there was any question about the correct text, those who were learning would go far and wide in search of an accurate and reliable manuscript, to make certain of the exact wording.

"It wasn't until the middle of the fifteenth century that Johannes Gutenberg invented the printing press in Mainz, Germany — a full two hundred years after our story takes place.

"But perhaps the main reason there were so few manuscripts at the time this story takes place," continued Rebbe Mendel, "is that in those days, the Christians liked to burn Hebrew books. According to some historians, Rabbeinu Meir of Rothenburg, whom we will meet soon, himself witnessed the burning of twenty-four cartloads of Hebrew books in Paris in 1242 or 1244."

Rebbe Mendel then continued his story.

*And so, when Levi and Yehudah had finished learning the whole Shas from their rebbe — who was also the rav of the town — and the Talmud was firmly implanted in their heads, they longed to travel afar, to the yeshiva of Rabbi Meir of Rothenburg. After getting permission from their parents, they turned to their rebbe, told him of their desire, and asked his permission and advice.*

*"Your desire pleases me," the rav said to them. "Although the roads are poor, and robbers roam the land, and the mercenary soldiers of the counts and dukes plunder all whom they encounter, those who go to do a mitzvah are never harmed.[1] Go, and may Hashem be with you, and may*

---

1. See *Pesachim* 8b.

*you have the merit of growing in Torah and yiras Shamayim."*

The two left their hometown with tears in their eyes. It took them three months to reach their destination. Some of the time they rode in wagons, but most of the time they walked. Finally, they reached the yeshiva — the yeshiva of the Maharam of Rothenburg.

Yehudah and Levi labored and rose in the Torah, and after three years they had mastered all of the Rishonim on Shas, including the questions of the Tosafos on Rashi. They became experts in halachah, by studying the decisions of the Rif, as well as the opinions of those who disagree with him. In short, the two were well-versed in the Oral Torah.

Then Yehudah and Levi thought that it was time for them to return home, because they longed to see their families again, and because they wished to fulfill the precept, "At eighteen, marriage."[2]

The two went to the rosh yeshiva. Levi said, "We want very much to return to our home, and we have come to ask the rebbe to give us his permission as well as his blessing."

The Maharam of Rothenburg said, "Indeed, you should return to your home at this time, for I know that you have learned the Torah well and that you will spread its light wider and wider. But tell me, my sons, do you know how to swim?"

Yehudah and Levi were surprised by the question. Yehudah answered, "No, there is no river in our town, and so we never learned to swim."

"If that is the case," said the Maharam, "it is my wish that you learn how to swim before you set out on your journey, for, as we learned in maseches Kiddushin,[3] there are those who say that a father is obligated to teach his sons to swim. Now, although nobody rules that this is the halachah, nevertheless, since there is such an opinion, I want you to learn."

---

2. *Pirkei Avos* 5:21.
3. 29a.

*The rosh yeshiva called over one of the students and instructed him to teach Yehudah and Levi to swim. A few days later, the two presented themselves to the rosh yeshiva again and said, "We have done what the rebbe instructed us to do, and now we have come to receive the rebbe's permission and blessing."*

*The Maharam then said, "Go in peace! But promise me, my sons, that you will stay on the high road, and not try to shorten your trip by taking paths that you are not familiar with. Surely you remember, 'There is a long way that is short and there is a short way that is long.'"[4]*

Rebbe Mendel made a *berachah* and took a drink of water. "As you know, my dear students, sometimes a person wants to take a shortcut, but in the end, because of this shortcut, there come upon him many mishaps, and it turns out that he is delayed much more than if he had taken the longer way. I beg you to remember this on your journey through life." And then he continued the story.

*Yehudah and Levi parted from their rebbe and their friends emotionally and began to walk home. For the entire trip they were careful not to go against their rebbe's instructions, and stayed on the high road. Many times they would have been able to shorten the way by taking one path or another, but they could not ignore what their rebbe said.*

*When two months had passed, and the two were completely exhausted from the length of the journey and eager to see their homes and families, they came to a fork in the road. One way, the high road, was wide and smooth, and if they had gone that way, the trip would have taken several more weeks. The second possibility was to go on a wide path through the*

---

4. *Eruvin* 53b.

*fields, which — according to what they had been told — if they would take it, they would reach their destination more quickly.*

The two stood at the crossroads and started to argue: Would the rosh yeshiva have permitted them to take a path like this one? After all, this path is like a road. But on the other hand, maybe this path cannot be called a high road. One said yes, and the other said no. One said, "Why court trouble? Let us continue on the main road, and not have any doubts." And the other said, "The rebbe did not mean a path like this, because this is not a shortcut, but a wide path, and it, too, is a high road."

In the end, because they were exhausted by the long journey, they decided to take the path, not knowing that they were stepping into the lion's mouth.

Several miles from the fork in the road, a monastery stood not far from the path.

After Yehudah and Levi had been following the path for half a day, they saw a group of Christian monks working in a field close by. The monks noticed Yehudah and Levi, and saw that they were Jews. They stopped their work and approached the two, saying to each other, "Here are two Jews. Let us seize them and force them to become Christians." (God forbid!)

The group of monks was large. Yehudah and Levi retreated apprehensively, but the monks surrounded them. When they saw that they were surrounded, Yehudah and Levi tried to break through the circle and run away, but there were too many monks, and the two bachurim quickly found themselves tied up and thrown into the courtyard of the monastery.

After this, the monk who was in charge of the monastery came to the bachurim and said, "Look here, you are young men, and it would be a shame for you to die. Accept the Christian faith, for if you do not — it will be your end."

Yehudah answered, "We are not afraid of death, but when the matter becomes known, you will be punished for taking our lives, because according to the laws of His Majesty the Emperor, it is forbidden to convert a Jew against his will."

The monk smiled maliciously and said, "And who will know that you were even here? After we kill you, we will bury you deep in the ground of the monastery courtyard, and nobody will ever find out about it. So think about it, boys: Christianity or death."

The monk left them, and Levi and Yehudah said to each other, "We are being punished for having transgressed our rebbe's command, but how blessed it will be to die al kiddush Hashem."

Every day, monks came and threatened the bachurim with all kinds of torture, but the young men were steadfast in their refusal to convert. Early one morning, after several days, during which Yehudah and Levi had not left the confines of the monastery, the monks dragged them out to the courtyard. There, twenty paces from where they stood, was a river, and on its bank stood a Christian symbol.

Many monks stood around Yehudah and Levi. One of them held a polished sword, whose sharp blade shone in the sun.

Then the head monk approached them and said, "Look: this is your last chance. Go to the cross that is standing on the river bank and bow down to it. If you don't, we will cut your throats immediately."

Yehudah and Levi trembled a little. Then suddenly Levi whispered in Hebrew, "The river will save us!"

Yehudah lifted his head, and his eyes met Levi's. The friends understood each other.

The monks looked at them suspiciously, and the one with the sword walked slowly toward them.

Levi and Yehudah left the place where they stood and walked with backs straight and heads held high in the direction of the "image." The monks looked at them full of satisfaction.

When Yehudah and Levi were close to the cross, they suddenly — without bending over — jumped straight into the river, feet first. They began to swim with all their might.

*Levi and Yehudah began to swim with all their might.*

*The monks were caught off guard, and by the time they recovered their wits, the young men were on the other side of the river and running as fast as they could.*

*Out of breath and panting, Yehudah and Levi continued to run until they were sure that the monks were not following them. Then they slowed down. They continued walking until they came to a small town, where they allowed themselves to rest.*

*The first thing they did was look for a Jewish house so that they could put on tefillin, for their tefillin were in the monastery with the rest of their possessions. To their great joy and relief, they found a Jew who warmly welcomed them into his house and lent them tefillin.*

*After they prayed and had a bite to eat, their host asked them what had happened to them, that they had nothing and their clothes were wet and torn.*

*Yehudah and Levi told the Jew about the mortal danger they had been in, about their refusal to, God forbid, convert to Christianity, and about how they had been ready to die al kiddush Hashem. Finally, they told him about how they had jumped into the river and made a miraculous escape, and about their rebbe's ruach ha-kodesh — as a result of which he insisted that they learn to swim.*

*The Jew listened to them attentively, and when they had finished their story he asked them, "And the monks? What did they do when you walked toward the river?"*

*"What do you mean, what did they do?" asked Yehudah, puzzled. "They were sure that we… " Suddenly Yehudah's face became pale and he cried out, "Oy vey! Woe is us! What have we done?!"*

*"Wh… What's the matter?" asked Levi fearfully.*

*Yehudah said nothing. He tore his tattered shirt and covered his face with his hands.*

*"Do you understand what is happening here?" Levi asked their host.*

*The man nodded his head sadly. "Don't you realize? While you were* taking those twenty steps, the monks thought that you were about to bow down to the cross. Because of that your friend is 'rolling in ashes.'"

Now Levi's face became pale. He sat in his place wrapped in grief and didn't stir.

Their host left them to themselves. A few hours later he came in, bringing a pitcher of water and two glasses. He found the two friends just as were when he left the room, Yehudah whimpering on the floor and Levi sitting motionless and depressed.

"Get up!" he rebuked them. "'There is a time to mourn and a time to dance.'[5] I understand your sorrow. But your task is to return to the place where you were born and to spread the Torah you learned. Don't waste your mission in life by killing yourselves with guilt."

Yehudah and Levi got up silently, drank the water that their host had brought them, changed into clothes of his until their own clothes dried, and later went to shul with him for Minchah and Ma'ariv.

At shul, the Jews of the town greeted them with "Shalom aleichem," but Yehudah and Levi only nodded, the way people do on Tishah b'Av, and stood at the very back of the shul to pray, like those who have been shunned by the community.

The next morning, after they had slept in the house of their Jewish host, they thanked him and set out on their way.

A half-day's walk lay between them and their birthplace, but instead of striding along happily, filled with anticipation, they walked slowly and silently.

They walked a long time without saying anything. Then Levi unexpectedly said, "I don't question our great rebbe, but it is a wonder to me that he demanded that we learn to swim. It would have been better if

---

5. *Koheles* 3:4.

we hadn't known how to swim, because then we would be dead, and we wouldn't have been *mechallel Shem Shamayim*."

Yehudah didn't answer, and Levi fell silent.

At long last they saw the houses of their town in the distance, and in less than an hour Yehudah and Levi were walking down the town's main street.

Some of the townsmen looked at the *bachurim* without recognizing them. They wanted to go up to them and ask what brought them to the town, when Gershon the milkman cried out, "*Baruch mechayeh ha-meisim!* It's Levi and Yehudah, our two prodigies who went to the yeshiva of Rabbeinu Meir of Rothenburg!"

The news that Yehudah and Levi had come home spread quickly, and the whole town gathered around them. Their parents tried to push through the crowd in order to embrace them, but Yehudah cried out in a sad voice, "Do not call us Naomi; call us Marah, because it is very bitter for us."[6]

All the townspeople looked at him in amazement, and then the two fathers succeeded in reaching their sons and hugged them with feeling.

"Thank God for returning you to us healthy and unharmed," said Yehudah's father.

"And surely as full of Torah as a pomegranate has seeds!" added Levi's father.

"Blessed be He and blessed be His Name," exclaimed Levi, "but woe unto us that we returned healthy and unharmed. If only we were dead, for we have desecrated the name of the Lord our God and stretched out our hands to a strange god."[7]

---

6. See *Ruth* 1:20.
7. From *Tehillim* 44:21.

Little by little, the townspeople left the area, completely confused, and the parents of Levi and Yehudah took their sons home.

Days passed, and Yehudah and Levi sat at home like outcasts, gloomy and desolate, mourning and overcome with shame.

When the aged rav of the town heard what was happening, he sent for Yehudah and Levi to come to his house urgently. With heads bowed, the two went to their rebbe and told him all that had happened to them.

Their rebbe looked at them with love and compassion and said, "Leave this matter for the moment. I called you urgently, because I have a very difficult question regarding whether a non-Jew is commanded concerning the halachah of yehareg v'al ya'avor."[8]

Yehudah heard the rebbe's question and answered immediately, "Surely this is what is written regarding Na'aman..."

"Indeed?" asked the rebbe. "But does that Gemara come to a halachic conclusion?"

Levi now jumped in to the discussion. "The rebbe is no doubt referring to Rashi's explanation of the Gemara there. But Tosafos understands it differently..."

For two whole hours, the rebbe and the two bachurim "fought" the Torah's war: this one questioned, and this one explained; this one built a tower of svaros, and his comrade came and contradicted it from the sugya itself and then proposed his own svara. The rebbe proposed his method, and his talmidim argued with him, until the sugya was made as clear as fresh water from a mountain stream.

During this time, Yehudah and Levi forgot themselves and their troubles and were occupied entirely in the labor of Torah.

---

8. See *Sanhedrin* 75a.

*Then, when they had finished speaking of Torah, the two sighed again and Levi said, "Woe to those who learn but do not keep."*

*The rebbe asked them, "Are you sure there is no atonement for your sin? Have our Sages not interpreted the words of Kayin, 'My sin is too great to bear,'[9] as a question: Ribbono shel olam, You sustain the whole world, and my sin You are not able to bear?"[10]*

*Yehudah said, "There is but one atonement for us, and for that we must beg God to take our lives for having been mechallel Shem Shamayim. Everyone knows that only death can atone for the sin of chillul Hashem."*

*"Slow down, my beloved sons," said their rebbe. "I will instruct you regarding what you should do to sanctify Hashem's holy Name. For it is incumbent upon you to know that Rabbeinu Yonah taught that the learning and teaching of Torah atones even for the sin of chillul Hashem. This is what he wrote in his book, Sha'arei Teshuvah — The Gates of Repentance.*

*"Now we will speak of one who has committed the sin of chillul Hashem. He will find atonement in studying Torah constantly, and in laboring in it, as Rabbeinu Yonah, of blessed memory, said, 'In sacrifices and offerings there is no forgiveness, but in words of Torah there is forgiveness.'[11]*

*"And now, listen to what I shall instruct you to do. First, teach as many people as possible the myriad halachos of the Torah as they were meant to be understood. Secondly, listen carefully to what I shall command, even though it will be difficult for you to do." Then the rebbe declared, "From this very day until the day you die, after each tefillah, you must walk backwards twenty paces."*

---

9. *Bereishis* 4:13.
10. *Bereishis Rabbah* 22:11.
11. *Sha'arei Teshuvah* 4:16.

"Walk backwards twenty paces?" Levi asked, astonished. "The rebbe is making our atonement too easy."

"Not at all," answered the rebbe. "It will be very hard for you to do it. But listen to me, and do not fail to do it even once. Even when you reach old age, it is incumbent upon you to walk backwards twenty paces, on account of those twenty paces that you walked forward.

"And you should know that years will pass, and your custom will arouse people's curiosity, and they will ask you, What is this thing that you do? Then tell them about how you sinned in your youth, even though you will burn with great shame as you tell them. And it will be of great benefit, for you will sanctify Hashem's blessed Name, because the story will be told to succeeding generations, and they will know not to be mechallel Shem Shamayim."

When the rebbe finished speaking, Levi and Yehudah felt better, as if a stone had been rolled off their hearts. They thought, "There is hope for us." Then Yehudah said, "Thank you, Rabbeinu, for your words. They were like water on a parched and tired soul. We take it upon ourselves to do everything you commanded, but a difficult question pierces our heart."

Then Levi continued, "As we said, Rabbeinu Meir of Rothenburg instructed us to learn to swim, and we thought that he foresaw with ruach ha-kodesh that we would save our lives by swimming — and indeed we were saved. But is it really possible that this is what our rebbe meant? It is obvious that it was forbidden for us to walk toward the river on whose bank stood the abominable idol."

The aged rabbi closed his eyes and said, "Am I a prophet? I am not able to comprehend the ways of Rabbeinu Maharam of Rothenburg. However, I will tell you my opinion: If you had listened to the words of your great rebbe, you would not have had to jump into the water at all, for you would not have taken that dangerous road. And if you ask, nevertheless, for what reason he instructed you to learn how to swim, I would say that you have many years in front of you, and who knows whether *you will need that ability in the future.*

*"It also occurs to me that it is possible that your rebbe intended to save you from the monks, for who can say what would have happened if you had stood stubbornly where they dragged you, and refused to move? You think that the one with the sword would have cut off your heads, God forbid. However, I think that if you had refused to move, the monks would have dragged you to their idol against your will and then dunked you in the river — for that is part of their abominable religion. But then you could have slipped from their hands like fish and been saved without a hint of sin."*

*Yehudah and Levi looked at their rebbe with admiration mixed with sadness, and Yehudah said, "Indeed, we are as nothing, Levi and I, both in learning and in deeds, and from now on we will take it upon ourselves to learn and to teach, to keep and to do."*

*Levi took the rebbe's hand and nodded wordlessly, his cheeks wet with tears.*

*Many years passed. Yehudah and Levi married and established families, and gathered talmidim, each in the place he lived. And at every tefillah — Shabbos and weekdays, fasts and feasts — they walked backwards the twenty paces. Even in their old age, even when it had become very hard for them, they did it. Supported by those around them, they walked backwards twenty paces.*

Rebbe Mendel finished his story, and we, who had sat the whole time without moving, felt as if we had awakened from a deep and distant dream. We sat quietly, until Rebbe Mendel broke the silence.

"You see, children," he said, "how important *kiddush Hashem* is. And if you think that *kiddush Shem Shamayim* means to die *al kiddush Hashem,* and that there is no other way to do this mitzvah, you are mistaken. You can sanctify

*Shem Shamayim* at any time with your behavior — even, for example, in *birkas ha-mazon*. When someone in the class says it with *kavanah*, everyone else sees it and says it with more *kavanah* himself.

"And there's another thing you should know: Every mitzvah a person does without getting any material benefit and without any expectation of honor, is also considered a *kiddush Hashem*."[12]

---

12. See Rambam, *Hilchos Yesodei haTorah* 5:10.

# CHAPTER 2

## *HOW TO CATCH A MONKEY*

**W**hen we were learning *parashas Re'eh* and came to the verse כִּי פָתֹחַ תִּפְתַּח אֶת יָדְךָ לוֹ, "You shall continually open your hand to him,"[1] Rebbe Mendel asked us if we had noticed the *te'amim* beneath the words פָתֹחַ תִּפְתַּח — you shall continually open.

"Yes," answered Yedidyah, "*darga tevir.*"

"That's right," said our rebbe. "Now, *darga tevir* is Aramaic for 'broken ladder,' and the Vilna Gaon says that the Torah is alluding here to a story about Rav Pappa. Once a poor man came to Rav Pappa, and because he did not help the poor man as he should have, he was punished. How? By nearly falling to his death when a ladder that he was climbing broke."[2]

Rebbe Mendel continued, "The words, 'You shall continually open your hand,' remind me of a story that I believe I heard from Rabbi Kessler of Bnei Brak. This is the story":

---

1. *Devarim* 15:8.
2. See *Bava Basra* 10a with Maharsha.

Once, when Yeshivas Me'or haTalmud in Rehovot was having financial problems, the Gaon Rabbi Simchah haKohen Kook, chief rabbi of Rehovot and president of the yeshiva, invited a number of wealthy men to a meeting. The purpose of the meeting was to provide them with an opportunity to earn the reward of supporting Torah learning.

However, after a few minutes Rabbi Kook saw, to his disappointment, that the men he had invited were not willingly going to donate generously — even though they could afford to. Consequently, instead of talking about the importance of Torah learning or the great virtue of tzedakah, he told the following story:

"Gentlemen, as you know, there are many kinds of monkeys. Most are caught in traps or with anesthetic darts. But there is one kind of monkey that is not caught in one of the usual ways, but in a way peculiar to it. I would like to tell you about how that kind of monkey is hunted."

The men who were present at the meeting had been sure that they were going to have to sit and listen to words of mussar and hisorerus, and had already prepared themselves. But when the rabbi said that he was going to talk about hunting monkeys, their mouths fell open in astonishment. Who would have expected a derashah on monkeys?! The curiosity of the rabbi's rich guests was aroused. They wanted to know the reason for his strange choice of subject, so they perked up their ears and listened closely.

Rav Kook continued his description. "And so, I will describe to you what a hunter does to catch this monkey. First, he takes a large, heavy glass jar, but one with a very small mouth, just a little bigger than a large nut.

"Then he takes the jar and cements it firmly to the ground. After that, the hunter takes several nuts and drops them into the jar — whose mouth, you remember, is very narrow. Everything is now ready for the capture of the monkey, and the hunter goes and hides in a place where he can see the jar and waits patiently."

*"Just a minute!" cried one of the wealthy guests, all of whom had been listening with rapt attention to the rabbi. "I want to make sure that I understand you correctly. Are you saying that the hunters don't put anything sticky in the jar or on the nuts?"*

*"Absolutely nothing," said the rabbi with a smile, and he continued. "No more than ten minutes pass before a small monkey approaches the jar. It smells the nuts and sees them clearly inside the jar. It moves closer to the jar, puts its hand into the jar through the narrow opening, and grabs a handful of nuts. And… that's it! Our monkey is already trapped."*

*"What do you mean, trapped?" burst out another of the guests. "All it has to do is take the nuts and run away. After all, the revered rabbi said explicitly that there is nothing that would make the monkey stick to the jar or to the ground."*

*Rav Kook smiled and said, "Indeed, the monkey wants to run away with its booty, but its hand is stuck in the jar, and it can't get it out."*

*"But then how did it manage to get its hand into the jar in the first place?" asked someone else.*

*"At the start," said the rabbi, "the monkey's hand was empty, so it was able to slide its hand into the jar. And it would have been able to pull its hand out as well when it wanted to if its hand had still been empty. But you remember what the monkey was doing — it was holding a handful of nuts. With its fingers closed around the nuts, its hand was like a fist, and there was no way it could get its hand out through the narrow neck of the jar.*

*"Now comes the easiest part of all. The hunter gets up from where he was hiding and walks at his leisure over to the monkey. When the monkey sees the hunter approaching it is terrified and tries to escape, but, because it is still holding the nuts, its hand is stuck in the jar and it cannot run away — and it is captured by the hunter."*

*"What a monkey brain!" cried one of the rich men. "It should let go of*

*The monkey grabs a handful of nuts and is trapped.*

the nuts, pull out its hand, and escape."

"You are absolutely right," said Rav Kook. "Indeed, a monkey brain! It sees that it is going to be caught. To escape, it has only to open its hand and give up the nuts. But that's it — it can't open its hand."

The room was quiet as the wealthy guests smiled delightedly at the rabbi's description of an ingenious and amusing method for catching monkeys, and at the stupidity of the unfortunate monkey that got caught by that method. But then the penetrating voice of the rabbi broke the silence.

"And in what way are we different from that monkey? Indeed, we know that 'tzedakah will save from death,' and it likewise saves us from terrible illnesses as well. We know that the world is full of troubles from which we may be saved by virtue of tzedakah. But we are in fact like the unfortunate monkey — we are not willing to open our hand."

Rav Kook then began to speak about the importance of supporting Torah study and the great merit of tzedakah. None of those present wanted to look stupid, like the monkey in Rav Kook's parable, so they all gave generously, with an open hand.

"And that, in fact, is the end of the story."

"What a wonderful story!" we exclaimed enthusiastically. "And how clever!"

"Yes," said Rebbe Mendel, "but there is something important you can learn from this."

"That *we* can learn from this?" asked Yehonasan, puzzled. "But we don't have any serious money of our own!"

"I know you don't have stores of treasure, boys," answered Rebbe Mendel. "When I said that you could learn something important from the story, I didn't have the mitzvah of *tzedakah* in mind at all."

It became very quiet in the room as Rebbe Mendel continued. "I was referring to the monkey's fist. Or, more precisely, to the trait of anger.

"Think about that trapped monkey. It sees that it is in serious trouble, but its clenched fist refuses to give up the nuts. And this reminds me very much of the quarrels and insulting arguments that break out from time to time among children — and also, too often, among adults.

"Believe me, a boy who has been humiliated feels tense and angry. He stands with clenched fists. He would have been much better off if he hadn't put his hand into the jar — that is, if he hadn't gotten into the quarrel — in the first place. Even if he wins the argument, he still loses, because his hand is stuck in the jar.

"If, however, instead of clenching his fists and being trapped by his anger, the boy relaxes and opens his fists, he'll get free of the 'jar' and win without fighting!"

"What does the rebbe mean, that he'll win?" asked David.

"I mean that he'll defeat the boy who was quarreling with him. Because to defeat the enemy with blows or a sharp word is a bitter victory; it turns the 'enemy' into someone who actually hates you. But if you give in, you completely defeat your 'enemy,' because you change him from an enemy into a friend."

Michael raised his hand and said, "The rebbe just gave me an idea. The next time we see a fight brewing, let's stick out our arm, open our fist, and say, 'Shake, friend!'"

## CHAPTER 3

# *NESANEL AND YOEL*

D ear reader, what I am about to tell you happened when I was a young teacher. At that time I taught in a school in the far north of Israel. Among the pupils there were many who came from non-religious families.

So it is clear that even if a pupil did not behave properly, the administration of the school weighed his case very carefully before they decided to expel him from the school. They knew that the pupil, if he were to be expelled, would go over to a non-religious school, and then who could foretell his future?

But, nevertheless, when a pupil overstepped the boundaries and there was fear that he would be a bad influence on his fellow pupils, the principal of the school along with the school supervisors — and with a rav's approval — would expel him from the school.

I would now like to tell you about an occurrence like that — in which a pupil was almost thrown out of our school.

In the class I taught, two pupils stood out: Nesanel and Yoel.

Nesanel, who was from a family that had returned to Jewish practice and observance, was outstanding in every realm: in learning, in behavior, in good-heartedness, in prayer, and in *middos*. In short, a pupil that every rebbe would wish to have.

The second outstanding pupil was Yoel. Yoel was from a non-religious family. His parents had not returned to Jewish practice and observance, but wanted their son to be religious. And so it happened that in school he absorbed Torah and *yiras Shamayim*, and at home he absorbed every possible poison — especially from that appliance that, in the words of Rabbi Shabtai Yudelevitch, *zt"l*, resembles a microwave oven in its appearance, but instead of heating, it freezes the soul.

Yoel was talented, but very difficult. In order to help the reader understand, I'll have to say the plain truth — there was in him a combination of bad habits that amazed me more than once: He disturbed the lessons, used words that he heard from the "microwave freezer" and hit his fellow pupils during recess (and sometimes even during the lesson). When he was punished, he would get back at the rebbe who dared to punish him. Once he was sent out of class, and a minute later threw a stone at the classroom window. The window broke, and Yoel was sent home for a week — a vacation from which he came back in a far worse condition.

When the principal hinted to him that he might be thrown out of the school, he answered insolently, "If only I would be. I can't wait to be thrown out. I'm sick and tired of learning here."

Nevertheless, despite the demands of the other parents and despite all of Yoel's actions, the school supervisor — in accordance with the instructions of a rav — postponed the execution of the evil decree — that is, the boy's final removal from the school. However, after Yoel's "cup ranneth over," it was decided that the next time that he went beyond the boundaries, he would be expelled permanently from the school.

Surprisingly, Nesanel — whose good qualities have been mentioned — and Yoel were good friends. Sometimes I thought that it would have been better for Nesanel to keep away from Yoel, but I didn't say a thing. I hoped that Yoel would benefit from this friendship.

A month passed from when we had decided about Yoel. During that month, Yoel visited Nesanel's house frequently, and the visits influenced Yoel a little. At the same time, I was happy to see that Nesanel was not influenced for the bad.

At the end of that month, during which, as has been said, there was some improvement, Yoel hit a classmate and was punished for it. I feared that Yoel, angry at the punishment he got, would take revenge on the school in some way. I prayed that he wouldn't, because, as I said, it had been decided that the next time Yoel crossed the line, he would be thrown out of the school.

The next morning, the walls of the school were sprayed with derogatory phrases about the principal and the teachers. True, there was no signature on the graffiti, but we could all imagine who had done the misdeed.

The principal called Yoel into his office, but the boy denied any connection with the deed. Even though we thought we knew, beyond a doubt, that Yoel was the one who had vandalized the school, it was incumbent upon us to conduct an investigation into the matter.

The principal came into the classroom and said, "There is no point in going on at length; you all know what happened. Does anyone know who perpetrated the deed?"

There was silence in the room, and then the principal said, "If you're afraid to speak because of *lashon ha-ra*, you should know that there is no question of it here. Therefore, I repeat: Anyone who knows anything about what happened should come to me and tell me what he knows."

Everyone's eyes turned to Yoel, who cried, "And who told the principal that one of the pupils did it? Maybe one of the cleaning crew sprayed the walls?"

"I didn't ask you," said the principal, "and don't talk without raising your hand. So, no one knows who did the deed? You should know that if we find out by ourselves, the matter will be much more serious."

The principal was about to leave the room, when Nesanel raised his hand. "I know who did it," he said.

"Yes, Nesanel?" said the principal. "Would you like to tell me privately?"

Nesanel's eyes were lowered, and in a quiet voice he said, "It was me."

The class was electrified. Everyone's face expressed complete disbelief.

"Nesanel," said the principal, "are you speaking the truth? Was it really you who wrote on the walls?"

"Yes," said Nesanel, his eyes still lowered. "I am a good friend of Yoel's, and I was very angry about the unjust punishment that he got, so I decided…"

"Enough!" declared the principal. "You and Rebbe Mendel come to my office during recess. I still don't believe it."

*"It was me."*

In the principal's office, Nesanel related how he had come to the school with a can of black spray paint and sprayed the walls. "Everyone thinks I'm a good boy who wouldn't do things like that," he said, "but in my heart I'm furious about the way Yoel is treated. This time my rage overflowed and I couldn't control myself, and therefore I did this thing. Now I am sorry and — I ask forgiveness."

The principal asked Nesanel to leave the office. When he had left, the principal turned to me in surprise. "I don't know what to say. Who would believe that Nesanel was capable of doing such a thing?"

"I'm sure he isn't the one who did it," I said. "I know Nesanel well, and it doesn't make sense that he would do something like that. Besides, when he told his story he spoke calmly and coolly. If he really were the one who did it, he would have shown more emotion. No, it wasn't Nesanel!" I concluded.

What can I say? Nesanel was punished, even though I was certain of his innocence, and Yoel was not punished, even though I was certain of his guilt. But it is impossible to punish a pupil when another pupil declares that he himself is guilty.

Time passed. Nesanel was once again the outstanding pupil in the class. As in days past, he gave us and his parents a lot of *nachas*. Only on his report card, under "Behavior," no grade was given for "Respect for School Property" — in memory of that deed.

Although Nesanel returned to being the Nesanel of the past, Yoel didn't go back to being the same Yoel. Little by little, he stopped being the class "bad boy." With much joy and satisfaction, I saw his improvement and praised him for it.

Months passed. Yoel's parents went abroad for two weeks

and invited Yoel to come with them, but the boy refused. Instead, he accepted the offer of Nesanel's parents to stay with them.

From then on, Yoel's improvement gathered speed. He and Nesanel set a time in the afternoon for a *chavrusa,* and because he had outstanding abilities, he enjoyed the learning. Now not only his mind, but also his heart, was captivated by Gemara.

After a number of months, Yoel's parents threw the "microwave freezer" out of their house, and Yoel's father began to attend the halachah classes at his shul regularly.

A year passed, and my pupils, including Nesanel and Yoel, graduated. Nesanel transferred to a yeshiva, and Yoel transferred to a religious high school. What I heard about Yoel made me happy, and what I heard about Nesanel made me very happy. Three years later, the two were together again in *yeshiva gedolah.*

One day I met them on a train going up north.

"Hello, Rebbe!" they called out.

I sat down opposite them, and I looked at them with pleasure and satisfaction.

Before I could open my mouth to ask how they were, Nesanel said, "Rebbe, I lied to you then!"

Then! It was immediately clear to me to which "then" he was referring, and Nesanel continued, "I want to tell the rebbe this, in order to fulfill the verse, 'And you shall be innocent before God and before Yisrael.'"[1]

"I knew that from the first moment," I reassured him. "I

---

1. *Bemidbar* 32:22.

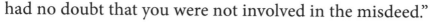

had no doubt that you were not involved in the misdeed."

Suddenly I felt uncomfortable — after all, Yoel was also sitting with us, and one does not allude to a *ba'al teshuvah*'s old sins in his presence. But Nesanel continued, "I simply knew that if the trail led to Yoel, he would be expelled from the school, and then there would be no chance that he would remain religious. So I took the guilt upon myself, and also prevented the rebbe and the principal from committing the sin of suspecting the innocent."

"You mean to say…" I cleared my throat. "What do you mean?"

"I mean that Yoel did not write those things on the wall. I don't know who did, but I knew one thing even then: It wasn't Yoel. I was just a boy, and I don't know whether or not I did the right thing. Today I know that a lie is very grave, but then, as a boy, I felt that I had no choice, that it was up to me to save Yoel."

"Yoel didn't write on the walls?" I looked at Yoel in disbelief.

Now came Yoel's turn. "No, Rebbe, it wasn't I who wrote those things."

"*Oy vey!*" I felt the blood drain from my face as I clapped a hand to my forehead. "I suspected an innocent person."

"*Nu*, I wasn't so innocent then," chuckled Yoel. "I want to tell the rebbe something. I stood then with both feet outside. I wanted to leave everything. Only Nesanel's hand still held me, as it were. Then came the graffiti incident. Everyone suspected me, and I, who was guiltless that time, felt persecuted and hated baselessly. The principal and all the teachers seemed malicious and threatening in my eyes. I decided that if they accused me, I would never be religious. And then, suddenly, Nesanel spoke up and saved me. At that moment I was moved by the magnitude of his sacrifice and I aspired to be like him. And the rest — the rebbe already knows."

Today, dear reader, Yoel and Nesanel are both God-fearing *avreichim*. And I want you to learn two things from this story:

The first thing: "There are those who gain eternity in a moment."[2] Nesanel gained in one moment not one eternity, but two — his and Yoel's.

The second thing: Never accuse someone unless you know absolutely beyond doubt that he transgressed.

---

2. *Avodah Zarah* 10b.

# CHAPTER 4

# AS ARROWS IN THE HAND OF A WARRIOR

My name is Tzvi and I live in Bnei Brak. I learn in a Talmud Torah that is part of the Zichru network of Talmud Torahs. In our *cheder* there is no vacation and no *bein ha-zemanim*. We learn happily every day of the year, including Shabbos.

Don't think that I'm bragging. I mention my *cheder* only because you have to know about it to understand the story I am about to tell you. The story is related to the Second Lebanon War, which took place in the summer of 2006. When the following events happened, the missiles were booming and thundering in the north.

One day — I think it was Tu b'Av — our regular teacher was absent for some reason, and Rebbe Mendel came to teach us in his place, for it was *bein ha-zemanim* in the *cheder* where he taught.

Right after *Shacharis*, Rebbe Mendel said, "I have heard that you are very well-versed in almost all the books of the Tanach, and that you know many *mishnayos* by heart, so don't be angry with me — I would like to ask you some questions."

Rebbe Mendel set three piles of cards on his desk — yellow, green, and red — and said, "On every card there is a question. The questions on the yellow cards are difficult, but not very difficult. The questions on the green cards are harder, and on the red cards are the most difficult questions of all — really genius level. A correct answer to a question on a yellow card will earn you two points, a correct answer to a green card will earn you five, and a correct answer to a red will earn you ten points. What will you do with the points? You will see that afterwards.

"The pupil whose name I call will come to my desk and be entitled to take the top card of whichever color he chooses. On the one hand, it pays to take a red card because of the number of points, but on the other hand, he might not know the answer to the question, and then he will earn no points. In each pile there are two hundred cards, so there should be enough cards for at least ten rounds — even if everybody chooses the same pile."

"What a great idea!" exclaimed Yehoshua, and we all agreed with him. I smiled to myself and decided that I would always choose the red pile. But you will see in a minute that thought is one thing and action is another.

When Rebbe Mendel heard how much we liked the idea, he hastened to say, "It's not my idea. My brother and teacher Yaakov, *shlita,* thought it up. When he came to test the class I teach, he 'invented' the idea, and I am only copying from him."

On the first round, everyone in the class took a card from

the red pile, but out of the whole class, only five boys knew the answer to their question.

On the second round, most of the class — including me — chose the green pile, and happily, everyone knew the answer to his question.

Rebbe Mendel praised us effusively and said, "Don't be upset because you didn't know the red answers. Those questions are very, very hard. Even the green answers are enough to crown you with the title *gaon*."

Among the boys in the class were three pupils who were "guests" of ours from the north. Two were from Tzefas and one was from Haifa. During that period, many northerners — who were forced to leave their homes because of all the shelling near the border — were our guests.

Chayim, one of the boys from Tzefas, took a red card every time, and always knew the answer. To tell you the truth, I was really envious. However, it wasn't bad envy, but *kin'as soferim*.

Chayim's friend, the other boy from Tzefas, took only yellow cards. "Maybe he doesn't know as much as we in our *cheder* do," I thought, "or maybe he does know a lot, but doesn't try the hard questions because he doesn't have so much self-confidence and is afraid he won't know the answers." I felt a little sorry for him.

After the seventh round, in which Chayim knew where in the Tanach the words *poom* and *feem* occur (*poom aryavasa*, in *Daniel* 6:23 and *feem le-machareishos*, in *I Shemuel* 13:21), and during the eighth round, in which he knew where in the Mishnah Rabbi Tarfon appears just as "Tarfon," without the title "Rabbi" (*Bechoros* 4:4), Rebbe Mendel got excited. He presented Chayim with a Parker pen as a prize, asking, "And what is the name of our *ilui* — our prodigy?"

"Chayim," said Chayim, embarrassed.

"He's from Tzefas," several boys called out when they saw that Rebbe Mendel was curious about the guest.

"Ah, from Tzefas! Welcome!" exclaimed Rebbe Mendel. "I thought that in Tzefas there are only great mounds of missiles. But now I see that there are also great mounds of *mishnayos* and *divrei Torah.*"

We smiled to hear Rebbe Mendel's words. Only Chayim did not smile. Hesitantly he said, "I wanted to say something."

"Please!" exclaimed Rebbe Mendel, "just don't test me. I don't think I will know as much as you do."

"I wanted to say," said Chayim, embarrassed, "that there are those who show off everything they know, like… like… like me, for example, who took only red cards. I wanted to show everyone how smart I am. And now I realize that what I did was not modest. I'm not like Akiva, the other boy from Tzefas. He may not want me to tell… but… I can't stand the pitying looks that the class has been giving him because he took only yellow cards. He did it because of his modesty. In fact, he really is a *gaon*, a genius, and an 'uprooter of mountains.'"[1]

We all turned our eyes to Akiva, whose head hung down and whose cheeks flamed red. "What is he talking about…" he murmured in embarrassment.

But Chayim continued, saying, "I am convinced that there is not in all the cards standing here a question to which Akiva does not know the answer. He picked yellow cards only because

---

1. See the story, "The Beautiful Duckling," on page 43.

*"Akiva is really the genius."*

he is modest and does not want to show how smart he is."

The room was silent. Then Rebbe Mendel said, "Thank you, Chayim." He didn't speak for moment and then said, "So Akiva, you are also from Tzefas?"

"Yes," answered Akiva.

"Tell me, please, where is Tzefas mentioned in *Nevi'im*, and where in the Gemara?"

Akiva shot back his answer with perfect aim.

Thus began a salvo of questions from Rebbe Mendel, and a barrage of answers from the modest guest.

"Which Korach was not involved in the controversy with Moshe Rabbeinu?" (*Bereishis* 36:5)

"How many figures in the Tanach named Shaul do you know?" (Three; see *Bereishis* 36:37, 46:10 and *I Shemuel* 9–31)

"What is the meaning of the abbreviation יע"ל קג"ם?" (Rashi, *Bava Metzia* 22b, s.v. *ya'al kegam*)

"Who are the fifteen women who exempt their *tzaros* and the *tzaros* of their *tzaros*?" (Mishnah *Yevamos* 1:1)

"Who was Rabbeinu Peter?" (One of the *Ba'alei haTosafos*; *Gittin* 8a)

"Is it possible that one may be obligated to separate *terumah* and *ma'aser* in France?" (*Tosafos*, *Gittin* 8a, s.v. Rabi Yehudah)

It was obvious that the whole business made Akiva uncomfortable, but he answered every question with amazing speed.

Rebbe Mendel nearly cried with emotion. "Akiva, you are a *gaon* in modesty," he exclaimed. He looked at us and said, "There are many *geonim*, but a *gaon* in modesty is really something." Rebbe Mendel put his hand on Akiva's shoulder and said, "The generation in which Akiva is found is not orphaned."[2] (These are the words of the Gemara about Rabbi Elazar ben Azariah.)

Rebbe Mendel then picked up a book and said, "Akiva, you deserve a lot more than this prize, but please accept it nevertheless."

So saying, he presented the book, *One Hundred and Fifty Te'amim,* to Akiva and said, "This book was written by my father and teacher, *shlita.* It discusses the one hundred and fifty times that the cantillation mark called *pazer* appears in the Torah, with a nice explanation of each one."

"What!" cried Yehudah, the third guest (who, as mentioned above, was from Haifa). "I didn't know that Rav Nachman is the rebbe's father."

"How do you know my father and teacher, *shlita?*" asked Rebbe Mendel, astonished.

"I am from Haifa," answered Yehudah. "My brother got that book as a bar mitzvah present from Rav Nachman, who reads the Torah in our minyan. Now that I know that Rav Nachman is the rebbe's father, I notice the resemblance between him and the rebbe."

"Your saying that I resemble my father and teacher is truly a compliment," said Rebbe Mendel. "What is your name, my dear boy?"

"Yehudah," answered Yehudah.

"Yehudah?" cried Rebbe Mendel excitedly. "Wait a minute! Don't tell me your family name… That's it! Your face tells me

---

2. Yerushalmi *Sotah* 3:4.

that you are Yosef Ariel's brother, and the son of Rav Ariel. Am I not right?"

Yehudah nodded and asked, "How does the rebbe know my brother?"

"Your brother!" exclaimed Rebbe Mendel. "After all, I was his teacher fourteen years ago, when I lived in Haifa. But something puzzles me.

"Every day I plead with my parents to move to Bnei Brak temporarily, until the war is over, but they insist on remaining in Haifa. My father even told me that there is always a minyan, and that the regular *shiur* continues to be given by Rav Ariel — may Hashem watch over him and give him long life — but I see you here. Did your father decide to move after all?"

"My father and mother sent the children to Bnei Brak, but they themselves are remaining in Haifa," answered Yehudah.

Rebbe Mendel closed his eyes for a moment and said, "See how a mitzvah brings another in its wake. I remember how it was fifteen years ago, before you were born. Then, not only was the north living in fear, but the whole country was seized by trembling. Missiles came from Bavel (Iraq), and it was feared that they carried with them poison gas. Whenever the siren sounded, people rushed to their sealed rooms and sat wearing gas masks until the all-clear siren sounded. People were instructed to carry with them at all times the little cardboard box in which dwelt the 'honored' gas mask and an injection in case, God forbid, the person was affected by poison gas.

"During the first weeks of the war, we were forbidden by the civil defense authorities to learn in the *cheder*. So Rav Ariel, the father of your 'guest' Yehudah, proposed that I continue to teach in his house.

"And that's how it was. For two weeks, we learned in Yehudah's house, even before Yehudah himself 'descended' to it. Because of his father, the learning continued as usual. And here, a mitzvah draws another. Right now Rav Ariel continues in his work to fortify Haifa with prayer and Torah!"

Everyone's eyes turned to Yehudah, who blushed all over, whereupon Rebbe Mendel said, "Boys, in *Tehillim* it is written, 'As arrows (*chitzim*) in the hand of a warrior, so are the disciples of youth.'[3] Because of the Torah that you 'disciples' learn so diligently, and because of the prayers that you say with such *kavanah*, you are therefore our *chitzim*.

"The word *chitzim* can be the plural of either *chetz*, arrow, or *cheitz*, separation. You both shoot arrows at the enemy and stand between us and the missiles. Know that you have a powerful weapon in your hands that no other nation has, but even with the best weapon, one must know how to aim it. Torah and prayer with *kavanah*! Remember that!"

---

3. *Tehillim* 127:4.

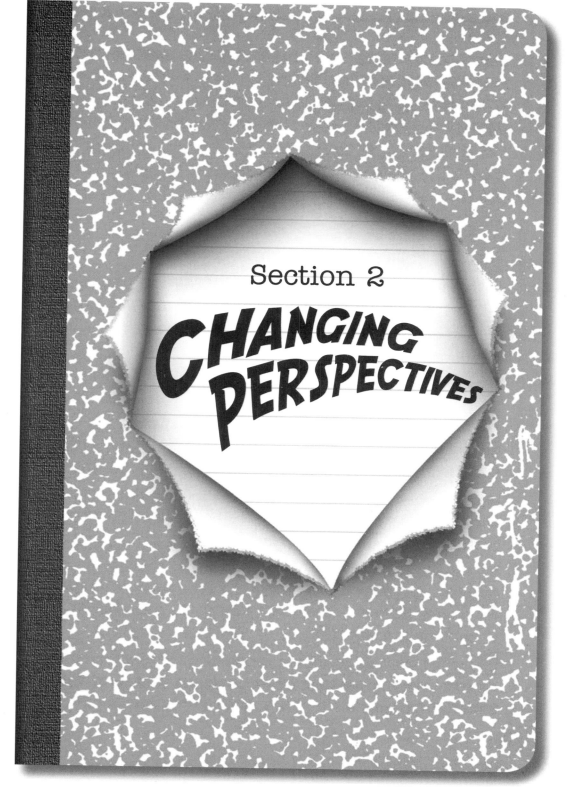

Section 2

CHANGING PERSPECTIVES

## CHAPTER 5

# THE BEAUTIFUL DUCKLING

Everyone knows that the two outstanding pupils in our class are Michael and Eliyahu. We knew it even in first grade. However, as the years passed, it became clear that there were definitely differences between them.

Michael stood out in his sharpness. He was always either questioning or explaining what the rebbe said, to the point where one day the teacher asked him whether he had drunk floor polish, and if that was the reason he shined so brilliantly.

Eliyahu was not as sharp as Michael, but, on the other hand, his *bekiyus* was amazing. He remembered everything he had learned so well that he knew whole pages of Gemara by heart. He was like a walking Shas.

We called them "Sinai" and "*Okeir Harim*," after a story in the Gemara about Rav Yosef and Rabbah. Rav Yosef was more learned than Rabbah. He could recall every halachah and every source, and was therefore called "Sinai" (because all the laws of the Torah were given at Mount Sinai). In contrast, Rabbah

43

was very sharp, and more clever in *svara* than Rav Yosef, and therefore was called "*Okeir Harim*" (uprooter of mountains). You can read the story yourself in *Berachos* 64a.

One day during our Gemara lesson with Rebbe Mendel, we studied the following incident: Two men were walking in the street. One was carrying a cask of wine, and the other, a cask of honey. Without warning, the cask of honey sprang a leak, and the honey — which is much more expensive than wine — began to flow out and fall to the ground. The other man — the one who was carrying the cask of wine — saw this and quickly poured the wine out of his cask and put the cask, which was now empty, beneath the one with honey, thus saving most of the more valuable liquid.

After the honey had been saved, the men began to argue. The one who had been carrying the wine demanded that the owner of the honey pay him what the wine had cost, whereas the one who had been carrying the honey said, "And did I ask you to pour out your wine? I will not compensate you for the loss."[1]

Rebbe Mendel had not yet finished telling us about the incident when Michael raised his hand. He was red in the face with excitement and waved his arm impatiently.

"Yes, Michael?" asked Rebbe Mendel.

"I don't understand," said Michael, his face even redder than it had been before the rebbe called on him. "After all, there is no reason why the owner of the wine has to give the honey back to the other man. The moment the honey began to run out,

---

1. *Bava Kamma* 115a.

its owner was *misya'esh* — accepted the fact that it would be lost — and so it's as if the honey is *hefker* — ownerless property. Therefore, the honey belongs to the owner of the wine."

Rebbe Mendel smiled at Michael and asked with mock severity, "Did you drink floor polish again this morning? That's a brilliant question you just asked!" Then the rebbe explained to the class the problem that Michael had raised.

Then we heard Eliyahu's voice saying, "But Rebbe, we learned in the Mishnah[2] that if Reuven picks up a coin from the ground with the intention of aquiring it for Shimon and then changes his mind and decides to keep the coin for himself — that would be stealing, because as soon as he picks up the coin for Shimon, it becomes Shimon's property. Now, the intention of the owner of the wine was to save the honey for the other man, not to take it for himself, and in that case, we learn from the example in the Mishnah that the honey belongs to its original owner, and not to the owner of the wine."

"Excellent!" said Rebbe Mendel, looking at Eliyahu with pride. "How wonderful that you remembered that *mishnah.* I'll have to look into this further and see if the commentaries discuss this."

We looked in admiration at our two classmates, the questioner and the answerer.

Rebbe Mendel continued the lesson, and within a few minutes we had forgotten the incident.

That day, Michael was unusually agitated, and at the end of the lesson he asked to speak to Rebbe Mendel.

---

2. Mishnah *Bava Metzia* 1:3.

"What is it, Michael?" he asked, and then added, "I was very pleased with you today."

"The rebbe must mean the question I asked — the one Eliyahu answered," Michael said, suddenly downcast.

"Yes," said Rebbe Mendel, "but tell me, why do you suddenly look sad? What's the matter?"

"I'm envious! I'm frustrated!" cried Michael brokenheartedly. "And I know that I'll never be a *talmid chacham.*"

"What terrible self-criticism," said Rebbe Mendel in amazement, "and the same day that you asked the very same question that the Pnei Yehoshua asked."

Michael was silent. Finally he said, "The rebbe must know that there is a difference between me and Eliyahu."

"Are you referring to the nicknames your classmates have given you in admiration — 'Sinai' and '*Okeir Harim*'?"

"Yes, yes! Eliyahu knows everything. He learns and remembers. That's the only way to become a *talmid chacham.* But I don't know as much as he does, and I don't have his memory, so what good does all my brilliance do?"

Rebbe Mendel hid a smile and said, "See me this afternoon, you and Eliyahu."

When the two boys went up to Rebbe Mendel that afternoon, he sat down with them and, turning to Eliyahu, said, "May I show Michael the note you wrote me?"

Eliyahu hesitated for a moment before nodding.

"Michael, you may read this note that Eliyahu gave me today, before you spoke with me, on condition that you agree that I may tell Eliyahu what you told me earlier."

Michael couldn't decide whether to agree or not. After hesitating, he said, "Will it help me solve my problem?"

"Yes," answered Rebbe Mendel. "So, do you agree to the condition?"

Michael nodded. The rebbe handed him Eliyahu's note. As he read it, a look of astonishment came over his face. This is what was written in Eliyahu's note:

בס"ד

To Rebbe Mendel,

I am so depressed, and feel so bad about myself. Although I remember well the material we learn, I don't have a sharp mind.

Michael, for example, will certainly be an important talmid chacham, but nothing will come of me.

I look forward to hearing your advice.

Sincerely,
Eliyahu

"Now I must tell Eliyahu," said Rebbe Mendel, smiling, "that earlier today Michael came to me feeling very unhappy, and said that he was sure that nothing would become of him, and that only Eliyahu could grow up to be a *talmid chacham* because of his great knowledge."

Eliyahu looked at Michael unbelievingly, and the rebbe said, "I will give you both an answer in class tomorrow. But I have a request to make of you: Please agree to let me tell the class about your complaints."

The boys looked at each other. "If it will do some good, I'm willing," said Eliyahu.

"Me too," said Michael.

The two waited impatiently for the next day.

The next day, at the beginning of the last class, Rebbe Mendel announced that the lesson this time would be *mussar*. We all put on a serious look. Rebbe Mendel began by asking if we had all heard the story of the ugly duckling.

We looked at each other unbelievingly. Had the rebbe decided to entertain us? The ugly duckling in the middle of a *mussar* lesson?

But to our surprise, Rebbe Mendel continued, looking perfectly serious. "For those of you who haven't heard the story, I will tell it now, but a short version — and one that is a little different from the original.

"On a certain farm there were both ducks and swans. Once, it happened that a duck and a swan laid their eggs at the same time. As a prank, one of the farm boys took an egg from the swan and an egg from the duck and switched them. The swan's egg he put in the duck's nest with the rest of the duck's eggs, and the duck's egg he put in the swan's nest with the rest of the swan's eggs.

"In the course of time, the eggs hatched, and from the duck's eggs there emerged cute little ducklings — except for the last egg. From this one hatched a chick that was strange-looking and different from the rest. The other chicks were unkind to it, and always called it 'the ugly duckling.'

"The very same thing happened among the swans. From one of the eggs there hatched a strange-looking chick, different from the rest. This one, too, was treated harshly and it, too, was given a cruel nickname, 'the ugly cygnet.'"

"What's a cygnet?" asked Daniel.

"A cygnet is a baby swan," answered Rebbe Mendel.

"Now, the two chicks — the ugly duckling and the ugly

cygnet — were sad and in despair. Each thought that it was no good. Because each was ostracized by its fellow chicks, they became friends. One day they decided to go to the 'rebbe' of the animals — the fox — and ask him what to do.

"When they told 'Reb Fox' their story, how each was called ugly, and was ostracized by its fellows, the fox answered, 'Neither of you is ugly, but you are both very foolish.' To the ugly duckling he said, 'Are you crying because you are an ugly duckling? Foolish creature! You are not a duckling at all, but a lovely cygnet!' And to the ugly cygnet he said, 'Are you crying because you are an ugly cygnet? Foolish creature! You are not a cygnet at all, but a handsome duckling!'"

Rebbe Mendel had finished the story, and now he looked at us.

"I know you are asking yourselves, What's going on, why is Rebbe Mendel telling the story of the ugly duckling in a *mussar* lesson? Now, pay attention and you will hear the answer.

We all concentrated as Rebbe Mendel began. "Nearly every one of us is himself sometimes the ugly duckling."

Then he explained his words. "The *yetzer ha-ra* makes every one of us think sometimes, 'If I were like him I would be as successful as he is. I fail only because I am not like him.' For example, the poor man thinks, 'If I had money, I would be able to sit and learn, but what can I do, since my lot in life is a hard one?'

"And his neighbor the rich man thinks, 'If I my mind were quick, like my neighbor's, I would learn, but what can I do when, instead of a quick mind, I have a slow one?'

"Everyone sees all of his own weaknesses and envies others, and in this way finds himself an excuse for not succeeding.

"In this, we are just like the ugly duckling. We struggle with all our strength to be a beautiful duck, instead of rebuking ourselves and saying, 'Stop! Do not try to be a duck, for you are a swan!' And instead of Yankel envying Berel because Berel is smart, he should know that he is Yankel, not Berel, and he has qualities of his own — for example, diligence."

Rafi raised his hand, and Rebbe Mendel called on him.

"How can I help but envy my friends? Not only is it hard for me to understand what we are learning, but I don't have a good memory, and I'm not a diligent student. What should I say to myself? That I don't have a good head or a good memory, and I have no patience to sit and study, but at least I am… what? What am I? Do I have any good qualities at all?" (That's the way Rafi is: he says what he has to say without embarrassment — "straight from the shoulder," as they say.)

"Rafi," said Rebbe Mendel gently but firmly, "you are making two mistakes. First, you are ignoring the fact that you are a beautiful duck, and think of yourself as an ugly cygnet."

"But what's good about me?" countered Rafi.

"Your courage," Rebbe Mendel answered him. "I cannot foresee the future, but it is already clear to me that if you ever have a problem, you won't hesitate to ask for advice, rather than stewing by yourself. You are not bashful or fearful — you are brave.

"The second thing you make a mistake about," continued Rebbe Mendel, "is your idea: 'I, Rafi, want to have a good head and the ability to sit and learn.' HaKadosh Baruch Hu wants there to be people who, even though it is hard for them to understand and be diligent, will nevertheless overcome their nature and will learn. And this difficult task He gave to you. If you will indeed overcome and learn through difficulty, Hashem will help you and give you both ability and diligence. You will not only have gotten what you lacked, but you will also have carried out your task and overcome your difficulties."

Rafi followed these words with bated breath. It was clear that they had made a great impression on him.

Then Gershon raised his hand and said, "But there are those who don't have to go through the trial of envy, because they simply have been given everything on a silver platter. For example, in our class, everything goes smoothly for Eliyahu and Michael."

Rebbe Mendel looked at Gershon and said, "Who says?"

There was a chorus of "Everybody knows," and "It's obvious," and "They have nothing to be jealous of."

Rebbe Mendel looked at Eliyahu and Michael and asked, "Are you sure that you are willing?"

The two were blushing, but they nodded.

"And so," said Rebbe Mendel, "I shall tell you something interesting. Yesterday Michael came to me and said that nothing will come of him, that he will not be a *talmid chacham*, because has no memory, and that only Eliyahu will grow in Torah, because of his great knowledge."

Everyone looked at Michael in wonder, and Rebbe Mendel said, "*Nu*, you call Michael '*Okeir Harim*,' and nevertheless he was envious of Eliyahu, whose memory is better than his own."

Everyone was silent, and Rebbe Mendel said, "In any case, you probably think now that Eliyahu is the best student in the class, since even Michael is envious of him. But listen! Yesterday, not only did Michael speak with me, but Eliyahu gave me a note, in which was written that he feels he is worthless, just because Michael is sharper than he."

We all sat with our mouths hanging open as Rebbe Mendel continued, saying, "You see, even someone who seems to have everything — the *yetzer ha-ra* confuses him with envious thoughts.

"Michael felt like an ugly duckling because his memory is not as good as Eliyahu's — instead of realizing that he is a fine swan with his sharpness. And Eliyahu felt like an ugly cygnet because he is not as sharp as Michael — instead of realizing that he is a fine duck with his memory and knowledge.

"Let us all look at what we have. Each one of us has something special that we can be thankful for and proud of. That is why Hashem made us — to accomplish our unique purpose in the world."

*"We all have something special that we can be thankful for and proud of."*

# CHAPTER 6
# *A TALE OF TWO AVREICHIM*

Reuven was a *badchan* — an entertainer at weddings. That wasn't his only occupation. The first half of every weekday, he sat in the *beis midrash* learning. The second half of the day, he taught young children in a school nearby. And twice a week, in the evening, he entertained at weddings, gladdening the hearts of the bride and groom and the guests.

The things that Reuven said while he was entertaining at weddings made everyone very happy and were even extremely funny, but deep down in those witty jokes there was a spiritual message hidden. Not that Reuven intended that at all; but because Reuven was God-fearing and also a *lamdan*, spiritual messages made their way into his entertaining stories.

The truth is that his relatives told him that he, Reb Reuven, was worthy of being a *maggid* — a person who gives speeches in public to arouse them to do *teshuvah* — but Reuven absolutely refused to consider the possibility, saying, "After all, who am I? What special talents do I have for such important work as this?"

But He Who causes everything, caused Reb Reuven "to answer Amen against his will."

This is how matters developed: One day, Reuven was very

tired, and had to struggle not to fall asleep at his *shtender.* He had been at a wedding until very late the night before, and despite this had gotten up early that morning. About eleven o'clock, he was told that there was an urgent telephone call for him.

"Reb Reuven," said the voice on the other end of the phone, "my name is Yaakovson. I am involved in the mitzvah of *hachnasas kallah* — arranging weddings for couples who have no money or no family — and I have an urgent request to make of you: can you come to a wedding tonight in Netanya to entertain the guests?"

"I'm very sorry," said Reuven tiredly. "When I started entertaining at weddings I made up my mind not to do it more than twice a week, and this week I have already 'danced at two weddings.' Tonight is completely impossible, because I can hardly drag myself around, I'm so tired."

"Please, Reb Reuven," begged Yaakovson, "I'm talking about a bride and groom who are both poor orphans, and will already be coming to their wedding broken and crushed."

"You've got to believe me, Mr. Yaakovson, I can't. I'll get to the wedding and fall asleep there," said Reb Reuven.

But Mr. Yaakovson would not give up. He told Reuven about the many troubles and tragedies that had afflicted the bride and the groom, until Reb Reuven said, "All right. Just this once I will go against my custom, for the sake of the unfortunate bride and groom. But you'll have to arrange transportation for me, because I'm just too tired to drive."

Reb Reuven was sure that Mr. Yaakovson would arrange comfortable transportation — a taxi, for example, or a ride with someone who was driving to the wedding from Bnei Brak, where he lived. So he was very surprised when Mr. Yaakovson told him that this was impossible."I don't have money for a taxi," he said. "Believe me, I've already put up a lot of my own money for this wedding. But you live in Bnei Brak, and there is a bus every hour from Bnei Brak to Haifa that stops in Netanya. Take that bus. It stops on the highway and doesn't go into town, so I'll wait for you at the bus stop and take you to the wedding."

After much more persuasion by Mr. Yaakovson, Reb Reuven gave in, and the two men arranged a time to meet. That evening, he was standing at the bus stop in Bnei Brak, waiting for the bus to Haifa.

As Reuven was paying the driver, he said to him, "I'm giving you an extra five shekels. This extra money is for you, so that you will do me a great kindness. Please wake me up when we get to Netanya."

"Certainly," said the driver. "But," he added, handing the extra five shekels back to Reuven, "I don't want money for it. Don't worry, I'll wake you up in Netanya."

"No, my friend," Reb Reuven said to the driver, "you don't understand. I am very tired, so tired I can hardly stand up. I know myself. You won't be able to wake me up so easily, even if you shake me. So what I am asking you to do is to open the door and drag me or carry me out of the bus. There will be someone waiting for me at the bus stop."

The driver looked at Reuven in surprise for a moment, but then said, "Okay, I'll do it. When we get to Netanya I'll pick you up and put you down outside the bus."

Reb Reuven thanked the driver profusely. He sat down in the eleventh row from the front, and managed to shout, "I'm sitting in the eleventh row, on the right side," before he fell into a deep sleep.

As it happened, the good-hearted driver hadn't heard Reuven's last words clearly, and thought that he had said "seventh row," not "eleventh row."

In the seventh row of the bus was sitting Reb Naftali, a *darshan* — a lecturer — who traveled from from place to place and inspired the public with his speeches. He, too, was very tired, but he had no reason to worry, because that evening he was on his way to speak at an Arachim[1] lecture in Haifa. And because he needed to get off at the bus's last stop, he could allow himself to fall asleep. He knew that when they got to Haifa the driver would wake him up so the driver could go home.

Forty-five minutes later the bus stopped in Netanya, where Mr. Yaakovson was waiting impatiently for Reb Reuven.

The driver got up and walked back to… the seventh row. Thus, instead of approaching the *badchan*, he approached the *darshan*.

The driver tried to awaken Reb Naftali. He spoke to him, but there was no answer. So he shook him by the shoulder, whereupon the *darshan* mumbled sleepily that he still had time — that he gets off at the last stop in Haifa.

The driver, who was intent on keeping his promise, didn't hear Reb Naftali's murmurings. He took hold of him with both hands, lifted him out of the seat, and carried him, sleeping, out of the bus. When the passengers looked at him in amazement,

---

1. Arachim is a wonderful organization dedicated to renewing Jewish values. They hold over two hundred seminars a year on five continents, in seven different languages. They help secular Jews re-unite with their heritage.

*The driver took hold of Reb Naftali, lifted him out of the seat,*
*and carried him off the bus.*

he said, "Don't be alarmed. I'm just doing what this fellow asked me to do." A minute later, the bus was speeding away from Reb Naftali the *darshan,* who was sleeping on the bench at the Netanya bus stop.

Reb Naftali opened his eyes. He was looking around in astonishment when an older man approached him. The man said, "*Shalom aleichem*, Reb Reuven. I'm Yaakovson. I can't tell you how grateful I am that you came to entertain the bride and groom."

"R…Reb Reuven? B…bride and groom?" stammered Reb Naftali in confusion. "I'm not Reuven. My name is Naftali, and I have no idea how I got here. I was on my way to Haifa, where I am supposed to give a lecture at nine o'clock." Reb Naftali looked at his watch. "Oy, it's already twenty to nine! I've got to find some way of getting to Haifa."

Mr. Yaakovson's heart fell. "You won't believe this," he said to the younger man, "but I've been waiting here for half an hour for a *badchan* who promised me that he would come to entertain at a wedding. Now I don't know what to do…. Wait a minute!" he exclaimed. "An idea has just occurred to me. Right, you just told me that you are a *darshan*? Please come with me to the wedding and speak there. After all, there's no way you can get to Haifa before your audience gives up and goes home."

"Absolutely not!" said Reb Naftali. "That would be nothing short of *chillul Hashem.* The audience is sitting waiting for me — and most of them are not even *frum* Jews — and I don't show up? I'll get a cab and go to Haifa."

"You'll never get a cab here; this is the main highway," said Mr. Yaakovson. "And by the time you get into town and find a cab, it'll already be after nine o'clock — and then there's the trip to

Haifa. So come with me and speak at the wedding," he pleaded.

Reb Naftali paid no attention to what Yaakovson said. He took out his cell phone and called Information to get numbers of taxi companies in Netanya, and then tried the numbers, one after the other, but his efforts were in vain. Not one of the taxi companies answered, and when, finally, he tried to call the lecture's organizer in Haifa, he couldn't reach him either. He didn't know what to do.

"Look here, Reb Naftali," said Mr. Yaakovson, "you can see that what happened is from Heaven. Reb Reuven, the entertainer that I was waiting for, didn't come, but Hashem sent you instead. Please, come with me to the wedding!"

When he saw that he couldn't get a cab, Reb Naftali accepted the fact that he wouldn't make it to Haifa. He was willing to help Mr. Yaakovson, but he was no *badchan*. He turned to him and said, "I have to tell you that I don't know any jokes, so what do you want me to do? It might be better if *you* entertained the guests with funny stories."

"I'm no public speaker," Mr. Yaakovson replied. "In fact, I suffer from stage fright. But you know how to preach. Please come with me and at least say something. The bride and groom are waiting."

Dear readers! As you have seen, Mr. Yaakovson was given great powers of persuasion. And so Reb Naftali agreed to give a ten-minute *derashah* — no more — so that the bride and groom would not be disappointed.

Mr. Yaakovson and Reb Naftali set out for the wedding hall, which was located at the edge of town. As they were walking, Mr. Yaakovson said, "If you can, put some entertaining stories into your speech. I'm sure that will bring even more joy to the bride and groom."

When the two finally got to the wedding, Reb Naftali climbed up to the band's platform, took the microphone and said, "With the permission of the bride and groom and all the honored guests: I know you are waiting for a *badchan* and are eager to hear some funny stories. I'm not a *badchan* by any stretch of the imagination, but nevertheless I have a strange story that I would like to tell you…" — whereupon he told the story of how he came to be there.

"And now, ladies and gentlemen," he continued, "I will tell you something I heard when I was young. About a month before my wedding, an *avreich* came over to me and said, 'There are two things you have to be careful about when you are married. First, when your wife washes the floor, never, under any circumstances, walk on it until it is dry. The second thing is, the moment you see a cockroach, kill it. Don't wait. That will please your wife.'

"As the *avreich* was telling me this, an acquaintance of mine — a very sharp young man and a *lamdan* to boot — was standing nearby. When the *avreich* had finished, my friend asked, with a scholarly gesture, 'One minute! One minute! What happens if you see a cockroach on a wet floor? You won't be able to walk on the floor in order to kill the bug, will you?'

"The *avreich* answered immediately, without hesitation, 'Well, Ben Bug Bug says you shouldn't move from Torah. So tell him a *vort*, he'll stay put, and then take care of him after the floor dries.'"[2]

---

2. See *Avos* 5:22.

The hall burst into thunderous laughter. When it was quiet again, Reb Naftali said, "I am happy that I was able to entertain the bride and groom. Mazal tov to everyone!"

As Reb Naftali stepped down from the stage, Mr. Yaakovson ran over to him and said, "Please, just another ten minutes. I see that everyone is happy, and the groom is glowing with pleasure."

Calls of "Let's hear more from the *darshan*" were heard from the guests. Reb Naftali told a few more humorous anecdotes, and then a serious look came over his face, and he began to speak of the *Shechinah* that dwells in a house, if those who live in the house have merited it. The guests sat motionless with attention, and Reb Naftali was unaware of the passage of time.

Finally, he said, "Anyone who gladdens the bride and groom, it is as if he has rebuilt one of the ruins of Yerushalayim.[3] It is my wish that we shall all merit seeing the complete rebuilding of Yerushalayim and the coming of Mashiach." Then he began to sing *Ani ma'amin* with great fervor. The band joined, and then all the men in the hall joined, their voices filled with yearning.

At last Reb Naftali was able to step down from the platform. As he accepted a glass of juice, the groom thanked him with all his heart, and Mr. Yaakovson was very pleased.

At this point, a tall man approached Reb Naftali, a man who, judging by the way his shiny new *kippah* sat uncertainly on his head, was not used to wearing one.

---

3. See *Berachos* 6b.

The man asked to speak with Reb Naftali. When the two had moved away from the crowd, he said, "Rabbi, do you remember who the young *lamdan* was who asked you about the cockroach and the newly washed floor?"

"Yes; why?" asked Reb Naftali, puzzled.

"It's important to me, though I would rather not say why just yet. Can you tell me his name?"

Reb Naftali strained to remember. "Wait! Wait!" he said. "I think it was the oldest *bachur* in the yeshiva. One minute — what was his name? Ah, now I remember! Berkowitz — Shimmeleh Berkowitz!"

The stranger smiled wryly and pulled out his driver's license. He silently handed it to Reb Naftali, who saw that it read, "Shimon Berkowitz."

"What?! It's you? Shimmeleh Berkowitz?" Reb Naftali burst out. "Shimmeleh, how and why did you…" Reb Naftali couldn't bring himself to say the words.

Shimmeleh laughed mirthlessly. "Hard to believe, eh? That you're standing face-to-face with the *lamdan* of long ago. Do you know that I finished the entire Shas with Tosafos and more before I left the yeshiva? But, as it says in *Pirkei Avos*,[4] 'Do not believe in yourself until the day of your death.' Actually, I once heard a nice *peshat* on that…"

Shimmeleh began to expound Torah, while Reb Naftali stood there, awed. Eventually, the two old friends found themselves seats, and continued arguing about one *sugya* and another, just as they had many years before, until the wedding

---

4. 2:4.

was over and everyone was leaving. Then Shimmeleh said, "I heard your *derashah*, and suddenly I missed terribly those days when I was so diligent in my learning." Then he sighed and said, "*Nu*, but there is no way back for me."

"What do you mean, there is no way back?!" said Reb Naftali heatedly. "Look around you and you will see that thousands, tens of thousands, are *chozrim b'teshuvah*, even people who didn't have a hint of a mitzvah to their name — and you were overflowing…. Yes, I know what you are going to say: what will my wife and children think, and what will they say at work. Believe me, that's all nonsense. People will get over it, and they'll deal with it. There is a great awakening nowadays. I say, you should be part of it before it's too late."

"But…" stammered Berkowitz, "see here…"

Then Reb Naftali grabbed Berkowitz by the shoulders and shook him. "Shimmeleh, Shimmeleh," he said in a voice filled with emotion, "come back! We'll decide on a time for a *chavrusa* for the coming month. Please!"

"What are you talking about, a *chavrusa*? I'm from Haifa and you're probably from Bnei Brak or Yerushalayim."

"I live in Bnei Brak, and we'll have a *chavrusa* by telephone," said Reb Naftali.

Shimmeleh pondered a moment and then said, "All right. I'm willing to learn with you *b'chavrusa*, and I will even take it upon myself to put on tefillin every day — my tefillin that have been sitting in my drawer all these years. But you should know that there is no chance that I will return to a Torah life, because even if I wanted to, my wife would never agree. Don't ask — she really hates religious people. Before the last elections she went from door to door campaigning for Shinui." (Shinui —

the word means "change" in Hebrew — was an anti-religious political party that fell apart some time after the events in this story took place.)

Reb Naftali laughed and said, "Don't worry, Shimmeleh, she will yet undergo a '*shinui*'!"

Shimon Berkowitz smiled, but then added, "And what about my son? He's a party activist — one of the most important in the youth wing — and an ardent follower of…"

"Don't worry!" said Reb Naftali. "One who comes to purify himself is helped from Heaven.[5] Let us do what we have to do and then we'll see. I've dealt with much more difficult cases."

"Hey, wait a minute!" said Shimmeleh. "You're talking as if I've already decided to return to a Torah life. No, never! What I said I'll do, I'll do, but no more. I like religious people, but to change my way of life? No, never!"

"I'm not asking for more," said Reb Naftali. "We'll put those thoughts aside. In the meantime, we'll learn *b'chavrusa* over the phone, and you will put on tefillin."

And the erstwhile friends parted cordially.

Let us leave both Shimmeleh and his thoughts and Reb Naftali and ask ourselves what happened to Reb Reuven the *badchan*.

✶      ✶      ✶

Our friend Reb Reuven was sound asleep. Suddenly he felt himself being shaken vigorously. He opened his eyes in alarm.

---

5. See *Shabbos* 104a.

At his side stood the driver of the bus, who said, "Sir, this is the last stop."

Reb Reuven straightened up, groggy with sleep. "We're in Netanya?" he asked.

"Netanya?" said the surprised driver. "We're in Haifa, sir. And this is the last stop. Can't you see that the whole bus is empty? You'll have to get off the bus now. I need to get home."

"In Haifa?" cried Reb Reuven in dismay. "But you promised me that you would make sure I got off the bus in Netanya! What have you done?!"

"Hey, take it easy!" said the driver, annoyed. "I kept my promise. I stopped at the bus stop in Netanya, opened the door, and even though all the passengers were annoyed with me, I picked up... I picked... Wait a minute! It was *you* who asked me to make sure he got off in Netanya? Oy! Of course! Now I remember! It *was* you. You're the one who asked me, but I carried someone else off the bus instead! That's all I need now! The other fellow is bound to complain to the company."

"If it weren't for the fact that the people in Netanya are disappointed, this would make a good story — and a very funny story," Reb Reuven mused. "A man gets on the bus, asks the driver to make sure he gets off the bus in the middle of the trip, and the driver puts someone else off. I'll have to add that to my repertoire of stories. But tell me, didn't you hear me say that I was sitting in the eleventh row on the right?"

"In the eleventh row? I heard you say the seventh row," said the driver. "I apologize. Please forgive me for causing you trouble. But you've got to believe me — my troubles are worse than yours! I'm sure you'll also make a complaint about this."

"Let's hope that no one complains." said Reb Reuven quietly. "Right now, I have to get back to Bnei Brak. Good-bye, and thank you for your good intentions."

Reb Reuven got off the bus, and it drove off. He was now in the middle of Haifa's Hadar neighborhood. He looked around, trying to find the stop for the bus back to Bnei Brak.

To his surprise, a young *avreich* approached him. "*Shalom aleichem*, Reb Reuven. Maybe you don't remember me. You entertained at my wedding, a little over three years ago."

"Now that you mention it, I do remember," said Reb Reuven. "You're Dudi Rosenfeld. How are you?"

"*Baruch Hashem!*" said the young man.

"Maybe you can help me, Dudi. Do you know where the stop is for the number 970 bus from Haifa to Bnei Brak?"

"Of course," answered Dudi. "It's across the street, down there," he said, pointing. "But you'll probably have to wait nearly an hour."

After a pause, Dudi asked, "Did you happen to see if the 970 from Bnei Brak to Haifa came? I've been waiting fifteen minutes for someone on the bus. I just stepped away for a minute."

"It certainly did come, about two minutes ago, and I was on it," said Reb Reuven.

"Did another *avreich* get off with you?" asked Dudi tensely.

"To tell you the truth, I don't know if anyone else got off," replied Reb Reuven. "I was sleeping like a baby, and when I awoke the bus was already empty."

"This is a pretty mess!" exclaimed Dudi. "I'm waiting for the *darshan*, Reb Naftali Horowitz. We agreed that I would meet him at the last stop of bus number 970 from Bnei Brak. You just said that the bus has come and gone, and the *darshan* isn't here. What should I do?" cried Dudi in despair. The young *avreich* paused and then said, "I'm sure you don't understand why I'm so upset. I'll tell you. I work for Arachim. Every two weeks we have a lecture for people who are interested in *Yiddishkeit*. The audience is waiting — but the lecturer hasn't arrived. Oh, just a second — my cell phone is ringing."

Dudi listened to his cell phone and then said to Reb Reuven, "That was the *darshan* on the phone. It was his number on the display, but all I could hear was noise. Just a minute, it's ringing again."

"Hello, Tzvika," said Dudi. "Yes, I'm still waiting. The lecture hall is full? Do me a favor and go outside. Maybe Reb Naftali decided to go straight to the hall. He called me a minute ago, but I couldn't hear a thing. Okay, I'll come right away."

"That was Tzvika, another Arachim worker," Dudi explained to Reb Reuven. "He doesn't know what to do any more than I do. I have no choice. I'll have to go back to the hall and tell the audience that there was a mishap and the lecturer can't make it."

"A mishap?" exclaimed Reb Reuven. "That's not a mishap, that's a disaster! Tell me, how many people are waiting there?"

"Two hundred young men," answered Dudi. "It was supposed to be a lecture for young men between the ages of twenty and thirty."

"Two hundred people took the trouble to come, and are waiting to hear words of the living God — and for nothing?!" exclaimed Reb Reuven. "That cannot be, my dear Dudi. Call a rav in Haifa, and ask him to come urgently."

"That's impossible. You see, this is not just any lecture. Our lecturers are trained to know what to say and how to answer questions. A rav who is not skilled, who has no experience with audiences like ours — he can make things worse, God forbid. Those young people didn't come to hear a sermon — even though they know that that they are going to hear a *chareidi* who will speak from the Torah point of view. Tonight, for ex-ample, the subject is the joy of life from a Jewish perspective. But someone who does not know how to handle the audience can do more harm than good."

Dudi's cell phone rang. It was Tzvika again, who told Dudi that the audience was getting restless and some were talking about leaving.

Reb Reuven closed his eyes and bit his lip in thought, and then said, "Dudi, tell him to tell the people that the lecturer will arrive in a few minutes."

"What lecturer will arrive? Who? Nobody will arrive!" said Dudi, upset and confused.

"Listen to me!" said Reb Reuven. "Call one of your lectur-ers right now and tell him to get to the hall as soon as possible. And until he arrives, I'll say a few words."

"You'll speak?" said Dudi frowning. "Well… why not? It's actually a good idea," said Dudi, warming to Reb Reuven's suggestion. "Tell them some interesting stories for ten, fifteen minutes or so, and that will give Rav Beinstock time to get there — he lives nearby. I'll call him now."

"Call anyone you want, but right now we have to get moving," said Reb Reuven, beginning to understand why he suddenly found himself in Haifa this evening.

Five minutes later, Dudi Rosenfeld and Reb Reuven entered the lecture hall.

\*　　　\*　　　\*

Dear reader, let us leave the bewildered Dudi and the resourceful Reb Reuven for a moment and go back ten days, so that we will understand who the young people were who were waiting so impatiently for the lecturer.

At that time there was a meeting of Shinui Youth. The young people discussed a number of issues in loud tones, and then from the back of the room there arose voices crying, "Wait! Quiet! Let Yaniv talk!"

Finally quiet prevailed, and Yaniv Berkowitz said, "Comrades, this isn't the way to do it! Our representatives sit in the Knesset and pass all kinds of laws, yet they don't know what's being done to them right under their very noses. They deal with all kinds of trivial things, like not to give money to the *chareidim*, but they don't know—" and here Yaniv Berkowitz raised his voice — "that in the meantime in Tel Aviv, in Yerushalayim, and also here in Haifa, right under *our* very noses, the *chareidim* are persuading committed secularists to become *chareidim*!"

Murmurs of shock and surprise were heard, and Yaniv continued. "Have you ever heard of the organization called Arachim? Listen, because of my father I know something about the *chareidim* — you know he was religious when he was young. Arachim organizes seminars in hotels and lecture halls all over the country, and from one of these seminars, the road to becoming religious is very short. Let me ask you a question: How many young people like us — committed secularists —

do you think participated in Arachim seminars last year? How many do you think?"

"Maybe a hundred," called someone from the back of the room. "No! At least five hundred," called someone else. "Three hundred!" "Two hundred!" Voices were heard all over the room.

"You see," cried Yaniv triumphantly, "you don't know what you're talking about. Don't fall off your chairs when I tell you the real number. More than *ten thousand* of our people — people like us! — participated in Arachim seminars in Israel and the world. They even go to India to hunt us there."

Exclamations of surprise and anger were heard in the meeting room. Yaniv raised his hand and continued.

"Comrades, listen! Every two weeks, the *chareidim* of Arachim give a lecture in Haifa. It probably won't be long before some of those who are sitting here this evening will fall into their trap. We have to stop it. If we don't do something, in twenty years Haifa will be as 'black' as Bnei Brak."

"What do you think we should do?" yelled one of those present.

"I've been waiting for that question," said Yaniv. "Pay close attention. In about ten days there will be a lecture here on the subject of the joy of life from a Jewish perspective. Today I saw a poster announcing it. I tore it down of course, but I read it first. I propose that thirty of us go there and show them what the joy of life really is."

Murmurs of assent and approval were heard and afterwards, applause. And then Yaniv said, "Listen carefully! We have to be smart. We'll sit quietly for a while, listening to the lecturer. Then we'll ask questions, and then we'll laugh and whistle, and then listen quietly again for a while. We'll let the rebbe say a few sentences, and then, once again… You get the idea? That should make them understand that it won't be so easy to turn our Haifa into a black-hat town."

Yaniv's proposal was accepted unanimously. And thus it happened that on the day of our story, when Reb Reuven and Dudi entered the lecture hall, thirty members of Shinui Youth were in the audience, waiting for the right moment.

*      *      *

Dudi looked worriedly in the direction of the energetic Reb Reuven, who whispered some verses from *Tehillim*, stepped onto the stage, looked at the audience of young people and said, "I was asked to tell you a few interesting and amusing stories until the lecturer arrives.

"Once upon a time, a Jew was traveling from Bnei Brak to Haifa by way of Netanya. He was very tired and knew that he would fall asleep and not wake up for his stop. So he asked the bus driver to do him a favor. 'When you get to Netanya, open the door and drag me out of the bus, even if I say that I don't want to get off. Just take me and — out!' The driver agreed, but an hour and a half later, the Jew wakes up and sees that the bus is empty and he is in Haifa. He went up to the driver and said angrily, 'Aren't you ashamed of yourself for letting me sleep like that?' The driver looked at him and said, 'Everyone seems to be irritable today! Yelling all the time. One passenger asked me to put him off the bus in Netanya. When we got there, I grabbed him and dragged him out of the bus, and he was yelling and screaming something terrible.'"

The young people burst out laughing, and Reb Reuven

remembered another joke and another interesting story and continued. The Shinui group didn't want to miss a single word, but nevertheless someone tapped Yaniv on the shoulder and asked him, "When?"

Yaniv answered in a whisper, "Wait until he finishes the jokes and the rebbe arrives, and then I'll give you the sign." Then he went back to listening with great enjoyment.

But Reb Reuven didn't stop telling stories. And why? The unfortunate Dudi Rosenfeld phoned Rav Beinstock and Rav Weinfeld and every lecturer who might be able to come within the hour, but unbelievably — and providentially — not even one lecturer could make it.

Reb Reuven continued to talk enthusiastically. He told another interesting story and another joke, and as we have already said, within his stories and jokes were planted many spiritual messages. And so, between the laughs, he wormed his way into the hearts of an audience thirsty for the words of Hashem. Even Dudi and Tzvika, the Arachim activists, couldn't stop laughing. But at the same time, they noticed the spiritual content of Reb Reuven's stories and thought that it would be a good thing to add Reb Reuven to the list of Arachim lecturers.

An hour became an hour and a half, and Reb Reuven spoke and spoke with enthusiasm. Then, after two hours, when Dudi approached him holding a glass of water and whispered, "It's getting late," Reb Reuven said to the audience, "You came to hear about joy in the Jewish way of life, so listen to this story: Once, a man came to a rav and asked him, 'Where is the joy in the Jewish way of life?' The rav answered him, 'Joy in the Jewish way of life? There is none. The Jewish way of life is itself entirely joy of life!'"

*Reb Reuven continued to talk enthusiastically.*

Then Reb Reuven began to sing *Ani ma'amin* with great fervor, and the whole audience (including the Shinui Youth, in whom some kind of *shinui* had taken place) joined him in song — without having any idea that earlier in the evening in distant Netanya, Reb Naftali had sung these same words with great feeling with the orphan bride and groom and the guests.

When Reb Reuven finished, there was thunderous applause, and many young people approached him in order to talk with the "rebbe." Reb Reuven, who was a *talmid chacham*, answered them according to what he knew, but immediately sent them to Dudi and Tzvika so they could get information about other lectures and seminars.

*     *     *

Yaniv sat on the couch in the living room, filled with thoughts about what had happened that evening in the lecture hall. He acknowledged that he did not know much about *chareidim*. He had always thought that they were lugubrious, that all the laws of the Torah kept them from even a little joy. And then this evening he saw a *chareidi* with a beard and *peyos*, a suit and a hat — who abounded in true, pure, unforced joy.

Yaniv was pondering this when he was pulled out of his thoughts by the sound of a key in the apartment door.

It was Yaniv's father, Mr. Shimmeleh Berkowitz, who had just returned from the wedding in Netanya. Yaniv got up and put a kettle on the stove. Then he went over to his father.

"Shalom, Abba," he said, "let me make you a cup of tea."

Shimon Berkowitz's eyebrows shot up. Never before had his son offered to make him tea.

Five minutes later, Yaniv came back into the living room and handed his father a cup of tea. Then he sat down and said, "Abba, I was never interested in the *chareidi* world or in your days as a yeshiva student, but I would like to hear some stories about your religious past — that is, if it won't be hard for you."

Mr. Berkowitz was dumbstruck. "Do you have ESP? All the way home from Netanya to Haifa I was thinking about my past in the yeshiva — and now, of all things, you ask me about it! Listen carefully, Yaniv. A remarkable thing happened to me tonight, a strange coincidence that I would even call a miracle. I was at Raphael Hirsch's wedding this evening…"

"Raphael Hirsch? The orphan? Isn't he your cousin's son?" asked Yaniv.

"My second cousin's son, yes," answered Shimon. "So listen: A *badchan* was invited to the wedding…"

"A *badchan*?" asked Yaniv. "That costs a lot of money. If I recall correctly, you said that Raphael was miserably poor."

"Money? What are you talking about? They had a volunteer entertainer. That's the way the *chareidim* do it. The whole wedding was made for the bride and groom. But forget about that for the moment. To make a long story short, they invited a *badchan* to the wedding. Everyone was waiting, but he didn't come. After a while, some *darshan* came instead of the *badchan* — someone who was on his way to Haifa, but to his surprise found himself in Netanya, imagine that…"

"What did you say, Abba?" said Yaniv, suddenly straining forward. "Instead of the *badchan* you got a *darshan*?"

"Yes, that's exactly what happened. And…"

"And what about the *badchan*?" asked Yaniv.

"How should I know?" answered his father. "I suppose he missed the bus."

"No, Abba, he didn't miss the bus. I'll tell you where he was."

"And how do you know?" asked Shimon.

"The *badchan* came to the Arachim lecture hall instead of the *darshan,* and I have to tell you, Dad, that it was a lot of fun — even though he managed to sneak a lot of things from the Torah into his stories."

"What?! You were at an Arachim lecture? I don't believe it! But who says that the entertainer who was supposed to tell us jokes ended up at your hall?" asked the father.

Yaniv smiled. "I know that because the *badchan* himself told a story about someone who wanted to get off the bus in Netanya, and by mistake someone else was put off. Think about that coincidence, Abba. The *darshan* who was supposed to go to Haifa ended up at the wedding where you were, whereas I heard the *badchan* who came to the lecture instead of the *darshan.*"

"That's no coincidence, my dear son," exclaimed Shimmeleh Berkowitz, "that's a miracle. I'll tell you more in a minute. But first tell me, Yaniv, have you started to attend Arachim lectures regularly?"

Yaniv stammered, "No. I mean, yes… no, not exactly. This was the first time, but it was serious."

"Don't be embarrassed. It would make me very happy if you learned a little about *Yiddishkeit* — even though I, to my sorrow, drifted away from that charmed world. But I often yearn for it."

Yaniv looked down. He didn't want to tell his father what

the original reason was for his going to the lecture.

"But," said Shimon, "I haven't told you the most remarkable part yet. When I was standing there at the wedding, listening to the *darshan*, I had a feeling that I knew him from somewhere. Then he told a story about something a certain friend had told him thirty years before. And who do you think that friend was? It was me!"

"So what did you do?"

"*Nu*," said Shimon, "I drew him aside and we traded memories. This *darshan* — Naftali Horowitz is his name — had been a good friend of mine back in yeshiva. Now tell me, Yaniv, isn't that a miracle? After all, if you remember, I almost didn't go to the wedding. But when I got there, I found an old friend who wasn't supposed to be there at all. And he told a story about me, not knowing I was there. And you're never going to believe this, but he managed to persuade me to learn with him on the phone every day. I agreed — and then, out of the blue, I volunteered to put on tefillin every morning. I was sure that you would laugh at me — and then to my surprise I hear that you are getting interested in *Yiddishkeit*, too."

Yaniv had been listening closely to his father's words. He then said, "Abba, this isn't just one miracle, it's a double miracle. Let me tell you what would have happened if it had been the *darshan* who gave the lecture…"

And Yaniv told his father in detail about the plan of the Shinui Youth to disturb the lecture, and how the plan was never carried out because of the *badchan*'s jokes.

Yaniv's father laughed. After a moment he became serious and said, "Yaniv, this is what we call *hashgachah pratis*. If you'd like, we can start learning together and I will explain to you a number of concepts you are unfamiliar with."

Dear reader, as was mentioned before, Mr. Berkowitz and Reb Naftali had committed to a daily telephone *chavrusa* for a month. But after a month, they just continued.... And what started out as a fifteen-minute *chavrusa* by the end of three months turned into a whole hour. Likewise, Yaniv had a *chavrusa* with his father, and learned new concepts that he never would have thought of in his wildest dreams.

*　　　　*　　　　*

Five years passed…

About a hundred *ba'alei teshuvah* were participating in a convention organized for them by Arachim. Among the participants were Shimmeleh Berkowitz and his son Yaniv.

Reb Naftali and Reb Reuven (who in the meantime had become an Arachim lecturer) were there, as was Dudi Rosenfeld, whom you remember from earlier in the story.

The purpose of the convention was to hear in brief how each of the participants returned to Jewish practice and observance, and to be strengthened thereby.

One by one, the *ba'alei teshuvah* went up to the podium and told the audience what started them on the path to *teshuvah*.

"I was a bus driver," said Shlomo Cohen. "I mean, I'm still a bus driver. And it was because of this that I became a *ba'al teshuvah*. One night, I was driving the 970 from Bnei Brak to Haifa, when a sleepy *chareidi* got on the bus and asked me to wake him up when we got to Netanya. I agreed willingly, but the *chareidi* went on to ask me to literally drag him off the bus and leave him on the bench at the bus stop if he didn't wake up. So what do you think happened?"

"Instead of him, you put someone else off the bus," Yaniv Berkowitz called out.

"How did you know that?" marveled the driver.

"I'll tell you afterwards," said Yaniv, and apologized for interrupting the speaker.

"When I got to Haifa, it turned out that the person who wanted to get off in Netanya was still on the bus, because, as the young fellow said, I had put someone else off the bus in Netanya. The passenger who ended up in Haifa instead of Netanya was very nice, and forgave me then and there. I was very surprised by the way he acted."

"I should be angry at you?" called out Reb Reuven. "After all, you contributed a wonderful story to my collection."

"What?! Was that you, rabbi?" exclaimed Shlomo Cohen in astonishment. Reb Reuven nodded and immediately apologized. "Excuse me for interrupting, Reb Shlomo, please go on with your story."

Shlomo Cohen continued. "I was afraid that the *chareidi* that I put off the bus in Netanya would complain to the Egged bus company, and I was very nervous that I would be severely reprimanded. I was also anticipating a heavy fine that would doubtless be imposed on me. So as soon as I got home, I vowed to give a sum of money to *tzedakah* (because even though I was not *shomer mitzvos*, I still kept some traditions). I also recited a chapter of *Tehillim*. Even though I was sure I would be reprimanded, I prayed silently that they would take into consideration my good intentions and not fine me.

"A week passed, and then another, and nothing happened. I wasn't reprimanded, and I was treated as usual by my supervisor.

"The matter aroused by curiosity, so I carefully inquired whether there had been a complaint about the 970 line. To my utter surprise, no complaint had been made."

The eyes of Shimon and Yaniv Berkowitz and Reb Reuven turned toward Reb Naftali, but he made a sign for them to be quiet.

"I thought very highly of that *chareidi*," continued Shlomo Cohen. "I couldn't understand why he hadn't complained. It was clear to me that if I had been in his place, I would have filed a strong complaint and 'made a lot of noise' because of the wrong that had been done to me. I thought a lot about it, and I came to the conclusion that the *chareidi* must have just forgiven me. I talked it over with one of my religious neighbors, and he said that it is even possible that the *chareidi* was happy about what happened, because 'suffering atones for sins,' or because 'everything that happens is for the good.'

"That is when I decided to look into *Yiddishkeit*. And suddenly, without my knowing why, there awakened within me powerful thoughts of *teshuvah*, which became stronger and stronger."

"Do you know why?" Reb Naftali suddenly cried. "Thoughts of *teshuvah* grew stronger in you because you were the one who caused the *teshuvah* of these two esteemed Jews." And Red Naftali pointed to Mr. Berkowitz and his son.

"Me? I brought about their *teshuvah*?" The bus driver was astonished. "I assure you that I don't know them at all."

"Sometimes a person brings about another's *teshuvah* without knowing anything about it," said Reb Naftali. "With your permission, I will continue your story for the benefit of the worthy people who are sitting here.

"And so," said Reb Naftali, after he had gotten permission to speak, "as you have already heard, Reb Shlomo put me off the bus in Netanya, and I didn't get to Haifa."

Shlomo Cohen looked at Reb Naftali in amazement, and the excitement in the audience grew as people began to understand what had happened.

Reb Naftali told in detail what had happened to him. Then came Reb Reuven's turn. After that, Mr. Berkowitz went up to the podium and talked about his past with great feeling, and how Hashem had orchestrated things so that he would meet his old friend Reb Naftali. Finally, Shimmeleh's son Yaniv completed the family story as you have already read, dear and amiable reader.

Then Reb Naftali went to the microphone again, turned to the bus driver and said, "Your only intention was to keep your promise to a tired passenger, and, from your point of view, what you did was a mistake. But without knowing it, you had a part in the *teshuvah* of this family, and so Hashem in His mercy aroused in you, too, a desire for *teshuvah*.

"That's the way it is: we all have a part to play in this world. And when we play our part, Hashem helps us — whether we know it or not."

## CHAPTER 7

# HAS THE SUN MOVED HOUSE?

My name is Ephraim Tzirman, and I am a *shochet*. I won't tire you right now with all the things that are involved in this holy work. *B'ezras Hashem*, you'll learn about *shechitah* in school. What I want to tell you is that a friend of mine who works for the same *kashrus* supervision organization was due to go to Argentina for six months to oversee the *shechitah* of cows, but at the last minute he had to back out for health reasons. Well, whom do you think they asked to go in his place? You guessed it — me, Ephraim Tzirman, a simple *Yid* who had never left the holy soil of Eretz Yisrael.

My wife Beila wasn't so pleased — and I certainly could understand her. However, being the *eishes chayil* that she is, she soon adjusted to the new reality and began to pack our bags.

"I'm not going to argue with you," she said. "I know very well that nothing will help, and that we have to go. I only ask that you talk to your company's representative down there. What city are we talking about, by the way?"

"Buenos Aires," I answered, "the capital of Argentina."

"All right. So tell the representative to find us an apartment that I will like. Remember, Ephraim, that you'll be out of the house all day, in the slaughterhouse and in shul, but I'll be in the apartment alone. I at least want to be comfortable in that *galus.*" She then proceeded to list another five or six requests. I listened carefully.

"Fine," I said. "I will talk to Mr. Blumenstock, my company's Argentine representative, to see that the arrangements are made."

"One more thing," Beila recalled, "I want an apartment with windows facing south-west."

"Fine, I'll tell him that," I said. "But why south-west, all of a sudden? Here we live in an apartment with a north-east exposure."

"That's just the point," said Beila. "I love to watch the sun set, and I never can, because our apartment doesn't have windows facing west. But it is more important that the apartment have a southern exposure. You see, the sun is always more or less to the south. Even at noon the sun is not directly overhead, but to the south, and apartments with windows facing south enjoy a lot of pleasant sunlight. So please insist that the apartment's exposure be south-west." [Dear reader, that is why rooftop solar panels in Eretz Yisrael face south. Pay attention to that!]

A few hours later, I phoned Mr. Blumenstock and told him all of my wife's requests.

"And don't forget," Beila whispered in my ear, "south-west!"

"Ah, yes. I remembered something very important," I said to Blumenstock. "We would like an apartment with windows facing south-west."

"South-west? All right," said Blumenstock. "I will try to

arrange everything in the best possible way. I hope you will be pleased. Good-bye for now."

Some days later we landed in Buenos Aires, Argentina, early in the morning. There we were met by someone from the community. He introduced himself as Menachem Weiserstein. He was very polite and helpful, and drove us to our new address.

When we got to the apartment, Mr. Weiserstein handed me the keys and said, "Here are the keys to the apartment. If there is any problem, you may call me or Mr. Blumenstock. You know Mr. Blumenstock's number; this is mine," he said, handing me his card.

We walked into the apartment, which, by the way, was very attractive and tastefully furnished, and I began to unpack. My wife suddenly appeared and said resentfully, "Huh! Well, he sure fixed things up for us, that Blumenstock."

I looked up from where I was digging around in the suitcase and said, "Of course he arranged things well. You see? You can depend on him. A three-room apartment, nicely furnished, very pleasant."

"I didn't mean 'fix things up' like 'put things in order.' I meant it like 'act dishonestly!'" Beila said.

"Dishonestly? In what way dishonestly?" I asked.

"In what way dishonestly, you ask? Don't you remember how I asked specifically for an apartment with windows facing south, how I pleaded for that? Well, look and see — we got an apartment with northern windows. The apartment is dark; there isn't a bit of sun."

"It is not possible that Mr. Blumenstock would do such a thing," I said. "He explicitly promised me an apartment with windows facing south. What's more, before we set out, he took the trouble to telephone me to tell me that the apartment he got for us faces south-west."

"And in the end we got north-east," grumbled Beila.

"How do you know?" I asked. "Maybe you're mistaken."

"*I'm* mistaken?" cried Beila. "No! Never! Come outside with me and see. You remember that the sun is never in the middle of the sky but is always to the south. We talked about that."

"I remember that we talked about its being a little to the side, but I don't remember which side."

"Try to remember," said Beila. "Right, the sun always rises in the direction of Itzkovitz's house?"

"Right," I said.

"And where does it set?" said Beila impatiently. "Try to refresh your memory!"

"It sets... it sets... One minute. Yes, its sets behind Warsaw Park."

"Exactly!" said Beila. "That says that Itzkovitz is to the east, and Warsaw Park is to the west. So, if Itzkovitz is to the east and Warsaw Park is to the west, and we are facing Warsaw Park, then where is south and where is north?"

"Just a minute, don't tell me!" I exclaimed. Itzkovitz is behind us — east. Warsaw Park is in front of us — west. Let me figure it out. That's it! I have the answer! North is to the right, in the direction of the flour mill, and south is to the left, in the direction of the candle factory. Hey! I have a sign to remember it by: 'The Showbread Table to the north and the Menorah to the south.'[1] Get it? Flour and bread; candle and menorah!"

---

1. *Yoma* 21b.

"Fine, you should be healthy, you and your signs," said Beila. "So we have decided that the flour mill is to the north and the candle factory is to the south. And to which direction does the sun incline? To the flour mill or to the candle factory?"

"You're right, Beila," I said. "The sun is always in the direction of the candle factory, which is to the south."

"That's what I'm trying to tell you." said Beila, "We got an apartment whose windows face north. Just have a look. You can't see the sun at all from these windows. And the other windows are to the right of the north windows, which means they face east."

"Just a minute," I said, "let's go outside and examine the matter."

We went out. "Do you see toward which direction the sun inclines?" asked Beila. Exactly the opposite of the direction the windows face."

"What can I say? It seems you are right," I said, and called Blumenstock.

"Impossible!" stated Mr. Blumenstock. "You got a south-west exposure."

Beila asked me to give her the receiver.

"Hello, Mr. Blumenstock? Forgive me, but what does that mean, south-west? Has the sun moved house?… What? You're coming over? Very good!"

"He's on his way here," said Beila. "It's really comical, how he says over and over again that the windows face south-east."

Half an hour later, Mr. Blumenstock was standing in the apartment.

He looked this way and that and finally said, "I don't know what you're complaining about. The windows here face south-west."

"South, you say?" my wife asked. "Then maybe you can explain to me why there isn't even a drop of sunlight in the apartment."

Blumenstock looked at us perplexedly and said, "You ask why there is no sun? Precisely because the windows of the apartment face south. A southern exposure is always darker, because the sun is always to the north."

"Excuse me — what did you say?" asked my wife, and she looked at Blumenstock as if he were a first-grader. "The sun is always to the north? Even a schoolchild knows that the sun is always to the south."

"Excuse *me*, Mrs. Tzirman," said Blumenstock, "that's just what I wanted to tell you. Every child knows that the sun is always to the north."

"South!" cried Beila.

"North!" said Blumenstock.

"Wait a minute — enough arguments!" I exclaimed. "I don't like arguments. But it seems to me that this time my wife is right. Because… I mean… How can I explain it? Where we live, the sun is always in the direction of the candle factory."

"I don't know where your candle factory is," said Blumenstock, "but if the sun is in the direction of the candle factory, the candle factory is to the north."

"That is out of the question!" exclaimed my wife. The sun rises over Itzkovitz and sets behind Warsaw Park, and that means that the candle factory is to the south. Besides, we live there, and it's *our* candle factory, not yours."

Mr. Blumenstock was angry; I could see that clearly. But he controlled himself and said, "Don't make such a fuss about this. After all, you are our honored guests. If you want, I will arrange another apartment for you, but for the sake of my good name I want to prove to you that this apartment has a southern exposure, just as you requested. But what you say about the sun is simply ridiculous, since everybody knows that the sun is always to the north. Let's go outside, and ask any passerby, and hear what he has to say."

"Very good!" said Beila triumphantly. "Let's go outside."

Our apartment was in the neighborhood where most of the *frum* Jews in Buenos Aires live. We went outside, and didn't have to wait more than a minute before a dignified-looking Jew passed.

"Excuse me, Mr. Eisenbach," said Blumenstock, "to which direction does the sun incline?"

"What's this — a school examination?" asked Eisenbach with a laugh. "Everyone knows that the sun inclines to the north."

"I don't understand what is happening here!" cried Beila in astonishment mixed with anger. "You can't move the sun from its place. And it is always to the south!"

"North!" called several people from the community who had gathered around us.

After twenty minutes there was almost a demonstration there: a hundred people yelling, "North!" and two hoarse voices barking, "South!"

Then Rav Ba'adani, a young *talmid chacham*, passed by.

"Rav Ba'adani," cried Mr. Blumenstock, "please help us. We are having a terrible argument. The respected *shochet* maintains that the sun inclines to the south, whereas we all know that the sun inclines to the north."

Rav Ba'adani smiled and said, "You're right!"

"Who is right?" was heard from every direction.

"You all are!" said Rav Ba'adani.

"So does the sun incline to the north or to the south?" people asked.

"Or maybe it doesn't incline at all," said Mr. Kunstadt.

"Listen," said Rav Ba'adani, "In Eretz Yisrael, the sun appears to incline to the south, whereas here in Argentina it appears to incline to the north."

"How can that be?" asked Mr. Kunstadt.

"I will explain," said Rav Ba'adani, quieting the crowd. "Does someone have a flashlight?"

A flashlight was brought quickly.

"And now," said Rav Ba'adani, "I need something like a ball, or maybe even a bottle, like the one you have, Reb Itzaleh."

Reb Itzaleh handed Rav Ba'adani the bottle of grapefruit juice that he was carrying in his shopping basket.

"Thank you," said Rav Ba'adani. "Now watch." He turned on the flashlight and pointed the beam of light exactly at the middle of the bottle.

"This is the sun," he said. "It shines on the bottle, which is the Earth. Do you see where the light is strongest?"

"Yes," said Mr. Blumenstock, "on the word 'Grapefruit' in the middle of the bottle. You mean that the sun shines most strongly on the middle of the Earth."

"Everybody knows that," said Eisenbach. "The middle of the Earth is the equator, and there it's hottest."

"One minute, please," said Rav Ba'adani patiently. "Someone

*Rav Ba'adani turned on the flashlight and pointed the beam of light exactly at the middle of the bottle.*

who stands on the upper half of the bottle — for example, on the bottle cap, which is the northern side of the Earth — where will he see the flashlight? Below him. That is, to the south, right? And someone who stands on the bottom part of the bottle — where will he see the flashlight? Above him; that is, to the north."

"Ahh," I nodded, "I am beginning to understand."

"And I don't understand a thing!" exclaimed my wife, who until that moment had been standing silently on the side. "I see that you are holding a flashlight and a bottle, and besides that, I know that for the next six months, my apartment will be dark and gloomy."

"Look, Mrs. Tzirkman…"

"Tzirman!" said my wife sharply.

"So — please pay attention, Mrs. Tzirman," said Rav Ba'adani. "In Eretz Yisrael one indeed sees the sun to the south, because Eretz Yisrael is in the northern hemisphere, the upper half of the Earth."

"Near the bottle cap," said Kunstadt with a thoughtful look.

"Whereas our country, Argentina," continued Rav Ba'adani, "is in the southern hemisphere, and therefore here we see the sun to the north."

"Aha!" breathed everyone in understanding, and the crowd began to disperse while many individuals showered Rav Ba'adani with compliments. Only Mr. Blumenstock and my wife and I remained where we were.

"Please forgive me, you were right," I said to Mr. Blumenstock. "I'm sorry."

"That's all right," he said. "And what does Mrs. Tzirman

say?" he asked, turning to my wife.

"Not a thing," said Beila. "I understand that there are strange things here, and that I won't be able to enjoy continuous sunshine."

"*Chas v'shalom!*" said Blumenstock. "I'll see today about moving you to an apartment with windows to the north, and…"

"To the north?" asked Beila skeptically. "Are you sure it'll be all right?"

"It'll be fine," I said. "I'm sure Mr. Blumenstock will give us an apartment flooded with sun."

"*Nu, nu*, all right," said my wife.

What can I say? The people of the Buenos Aires Jewish community were very kind, and two days later we were settled as comfortably as possible in an apartment with north-west exposures that was warm as it should be, to my wife's satisfaction.

In the course of the half-year that we passed there, my wife sat a lot in an easy chair on the northern balcony, holding a bottle of orange juice in one hand and a flashlight in the other, trying in vain to understand exactly what happens.

Maybe there is a difference between a bottle of orange juice and a bottle of grapefruit juice. Who knows?

# CHAPTER 8

## *POTATO PEELINGS*

"The story I am going to tell you now," said Rebbe Mendel, "took place about ten years ago, when I was still a young rebbe." The class fell silent and Rebbe Mendel began his story.

"At the time of this story, I taught in an elementary school in the far north of the country. As I have already mentioned in the story "Nesanel and Yoel," in the school there were children from families that did not keep Torah and *mitzvos*, but whose parents nevertheless wanted their children to get some idea of *Yiddishkeit*. And generally these children went from that school to a religious high school, and from there to a yeshiva.

"One of the boys in the class, whose name was Ronen, was crazy about soccer, and we had a hard time persuading him not to play soccer on Shabbos.

"One day we were learning the verse, 'The earth shall be as full of the knowledge of Hashem as the waters covering the sea.'[1] This is interpreted to mean that in the days of Mashiach, all we

---

1. See *Yeshayahu* 11:9.

will want to do will be to learn Torah and keep *mitzvos*. When I said this, Ronen raised his hand and asked plaintively, 'Won't there be even one person who will want to play soccer?'

"'I'm not a prophet,' I answered him, 'but according to my understanding, no one will be interested in trivial pursuits — but only and exclusively in Torah and *mitzvos*.'

"'In that case, maybe it's not worth having Mashiach arrive [God forbid],' said the pupil hesitantly, 'because nobody will want to play soccer with me.'

"'But my dear Ronen,' I explained to him, 'you, too, will have no desire to play soccer, and you will have great pleasure from learning Torah.'

"'No!' persisted Ronen, 'I will want to play soccer, and no one will want to play with me, because they will all be learning Torah.'

"I stood before him helplessly. What could I say to a boy who was so far from things of the spirit that he couldn't understand that there could be no enjoyment greater than learning Torah? I prayed silently to Hashem that He give me the right words to say. And then, with Hashem's help, I suddenly got an idea.

"'Listen carefully, Ronen,' I said to him, 'because for your sake, I am going to tell everyone a story now.'"

*There was a family living in Poland during the Second World War. There were two children in the family, a five-year-old girl and a three-year-old boy. The family planned to flee from Poland to Eretz Yisrael. First, the mother and the daughter fled, and afterwards, according to their plan, the father and the young son were supposed to run away. But the father wasn't able to escape, and thus remained in conquered*

*Poland. After a short time, the father was taken to a forced labor camp and succeeded through a miracle to take his young son with him and to hide him from the Germans, may their names be blotted out.*

*Father and son spent four whole years in the camp, and during all of that time the boy was hidden. The whole day passed for him in hunger and boredom. Only in the evening his father came to the boy's hiding place, bringing "delicacies": a cup of muddy water, a piece of stale bread, and some potato peelings.*

*The boy, who was already seven years old, didn't remember any-thing of his infancy and didn't know that there was a world other than the one he knew: the pit in which he was hidden, the barbed-wire fences that surrounded the camp, the cries and shouts, and the "delicacies." The unfortunate child had no idea that there was a different world, that there were people outside the camp who didn't have to hide, that there were a mother and a sister, that there was a house. He knew only the camp. And the sweetest time for him was the moment his father arrived with the moldy bread, the water, and the potato peelings.*

*A day came when rumors reached the camp that Germany had lost the war. That evening the father arrived and, his face shining, told his his son, "Listen, my dear son. You have no idea what bliss awaits us. Soon we will be free and will leave this Gehinnom. We will go to Eretz Yisrael, we will rejoin your mother and your sister, and we will have a house of our own. You will be able to run, to breathe fresh air, and to play with friends. You'll see how wonderful it will be!"*

*The son looked at his joyful father with a serious face and said, "Dear Father, I'll tell you the truth: I don't know what you're talking about. I don't know what a mother or a sister is, I don't know what friends or games are. If you say they are good things, then of course I believe you. But I want to ask you a question: Will you continue to visit me every evening to bring me potato peelings?"*

*The father laughed. "Will I come visit you every evening? Why, I will*

*In the evening, the boy's father would bring him a cup of muddy water, a piece of stale bread, and some potato peelings.*

be with you the whole day! And I will give you delicacies to eat: ice cream, pretzels, candies, and many, many tasty things that you haven't had the good fortune to know yet."

"I don't know any of those foods," said the son, "but if you say so, surely they are tasty. But you still haven't told me if there, too, in the house to which we shall go, I will get potato peelings every day."

"Potato peelings? Why?" exclaimed the father. "You will eat actual potatoes, plus meat, chicken, fish, and all the good food in the world! But I will not be able to give you potato peelings, because they are not healthy at all."

"Oy, Father!" wept the child, "please promise me that even in the new house to which we shall go you will give me potato peelings to eat. There is nothing in the world I love more than potato peelings."

The father was perplexed. He didn't want to lie, but he couldn't promise. For even if he had no choice but to agree to give the boy potato peelings, the boy's mother would certainly oppose it. Therefore he said, "My son, you do not yet understand, but I cannot promise you that you will eat potato peelings."

The boy looked at his father and burst into tears. "Please, father, don't take me away from here! I would rather remain confined in this pit and peek out at barbed-wire fences, if only I am privileged to eat potato peelings."

"That is the end of the story I told the pupils in that class," said Rebbe Mendel. "Then I turned to Ronen and asked him, 'Do you understand, Ronen? Do you know who the boy in the story is?'

"Ronen, who was an intelligent boy, understood well and lowered his eyes. But there were a number of children who didn't understand, and one of them asked, 'Who is the boy in the story? How does Ronen know him? Is he a relative of his?'

"'Would you allow me, Ronen,' I asked, 'to explain to your classmates who the boy is who did not want to leave that terrible camp?'

"Ronen nodded his agreement, and I said to the class, 'Children, the boy who wanted to stay in the forced labor camp so he wouldn't lose his potato peelings — that boy is Ronen himself, who would rather Mashiach not come (God forbid), so that he can continue to play soccer. He doesn't want to give up his pointless amusements because he cannot even imagine the sweetness of Torah.

"'But in truth, children, Ronen is not to blame — just as the boy in the story is not to blame. The boy had absolutely no idea that there is a different life outside the German forced labor camp. If he had known the sweetness of normal food, of freedom and open space, of family and of the wonderful life that he lacked — he would have thrown away his potato peelings immediately and run after his father.

"'And this is in truth what will happen when Mashiach comes. We will suddenly feel the wonderful sweetness of Torah and *mitzvos*, and will gladly throw away all things foolish and worthless.'"

Rebbe Mendel finished the story and gave us a penetrating look. "Tell me the truth. Aren't you feeling a little bit of contempt for that Ronen?"

We were silent, and Rebbe Mendel said, "I have good news for you, and also for myself: All of us act exactly like that boy and his potato peelings.

"Do we mourn with all our heart over the destruction of the *Beis haMikdash*? Do we have the same *kavanah* when we say the blessings '*Boneh Yerushalayim*' and '*Matzmiach keren yeshuah'* as we do in *'Refa'einu'* and *'Shema koleinu'*? True, we want Mashiach to come, because we know that when he arrives, *b'ezras Hashem*, the Jewish People will no longer have troubles. And sometimes, when we are on a higher level, we also think about Hashem's glory and honor that will increase in the world when Mashiach comes. But we have no concept whatsoever of the wonderful lives we will have then. We are imprisoned in our slave labor camp, and we have no idea how much we lack because there is no *Beis haMikdash*. If we knew and understood, we would mourn wholeheartedly over the absence of our holy Temple, and we would pray with all our might for Mashiach."

Rebbe Mendel let us digest this quietly for a few minutes, then spoke again.

"There is a verse in *Shir haShirim* that says, 'Pull me, we will run after You.'[2] Now, why is it written that we will run after Hashem? After all, if He pulls us, we no longer have to run — for we are already connected to Him. But the truth is, we really do have to run after Hashem all the time, but we are imprisoned in our daily lives and don't understand how sweet it is to run after Him. Therefore we pray, 'Pull me' — pull us out of our prison, and then, when we will be outside of it — not tied to trivialities and foolishness — immediately 'we will run after You.' We will immediately run after Hashem, because we will understand how sweet it is."

---

2. *Shir haShirim* 1:4.

Section 3

LAUGH LESSONS

# CHAPTER 9

# SELLING THE CHAMETZ

**W**inter was almost over, and we kids were getting a bit rambunctious in class. Rebbe Mendel decided to settle us down with the following story.

Pesach was coming, and preparations for the festival were at their peak. From the kitchen came the smells of Pesach cooking, and the whole house sparkled. The whole house? Not exactly — really, the whole house except, of course, the fifth room.

No doubt you are curious about that fifth room. It's really just a half room, and we don't clean it for Pesach. Just the opposite: we put all the chametz there, and what's more, until the hour after which it is no longer permissible to eat chametz, we eat there. Of course, before *sof zeman biur chametz* — the last moment for burning the chametz — we close and lock the door. We also hang up a sign saying "Sold to a non-Jew" — meaning that from that time until Pesach is over, the room doesn't belong to us. (We sell to a non-Jew only the chametz itself and any product that contains chametz; the room is only rented to the non-Jew, but not sold to him.)

So, the year in which this story took place the whole house sparkled (except for the fifth room, of course), and from back-yards and empty lots the smoke and smells from the burning chametz rose into the quiet air. Then, forty-five minutes before the time one can no longer own any chametz, I struck my forehead with my palm and cried aloud, "Oy vey!"

The whole family came running to me. "What happened? What's the matter? Are you all right?" they asked anxiously. And I, pale as a sheet, stammered, "Chametz… the chametz… the chametz isn't sold."

"What do you mean? What was wrong with the sale?" one of my children asked.

"Nothing, nothing is wrong with the sale. I mean, there was no sale. I completely forgot to go to the rav and make him my agent for selling our chametz."

My consternation and confusion lasted for half a minute, and then I was out the door and on my way to the rav's house at a run.

Four minutes later I was back with the bad news that I had not found the rav at home. (At that time we were living in a small town near Haifa, and all the selling of chametz over there was taken care of by just one rav, the rav I had run to see.)

"I haven't sold the chametz and there's only forty minutes left!" I cried aloud in panic. The only thing I could think of to do was clean the room and throw all the chametz into the dumpster at the end of the street. I ran to the room. But then the voice of my oldest son interrupted my grand plan-making.

"Abba, have you forgotten about Abdul Abu Azizi?"

"You mean…?"

"Of course! Why not?" answered my son.

Ten minutes passed, during which I found out over the telephone exactly how to go about selling the chametz and renting the room. Another five minutes went by, and I was sitting in the house of my Arab neighbor, explaining that I wanted him to rent from me a certain room in my house for the duration of the coming holiday, and to buy from me all the chametz and all the products containing chametz that were in that room.

I don't have to tell you that I was impatient. The hands of the clock showed that in just fifteen minutes I had to say "*Kol chamira*," nullifying all the chametz in my possession, but my Arab neighbor was relaxed and in no hurry. He was also a little suspicious. He knew that for one week every spring the Jews ate no bread, but he had never heard of this custom of the Jews, and he thought there was something fishy about it. Finally he accepted my explanations and said, "Fine. If I can help you out, why not?" Then he frowned and asked, "And how much is this going to cost me?"

I told him that for one shekel, the room would be his for the week of Pesach, and that I would amply reward him for his kindness.

"Agreed," he said. He gave me a shekel, and in return, I gave him the key to the room.

I ran home and said with great fervor the formula nullifying all the chametz in my possession. This, of course, did not include the chametz in the fifth room, which was no longer in my possession. The actual burning of the small amount of chametz that I had not sold had been taken care of by my sons while I was at Abu Azizi's house.

After that, I put a sign on the door to the room saying, "Sold to Abdul Abu Azizi." I did not write, as I usually did, "Sold to a *Goy*," because I thought my Arab neighbor might be offended by that. One of my sons asked me if my mind was now at rest. I told him not entirely, because the day before, the room had not yet been sold, and it may be that I should have done *bedikas chametz* in there too.

Be that as it may, I sighed a great sigh of relief and welcomed the festival with joy. It was at this point that the story really begins.

In the middle of the Seder, when we had just finished singing "*Dayeinu*," we heard a hesitant knocking at the door. When the door was opened, Fa'iz, the twenty-year-old son of our Arab neighbor Abu Azizi, came into our sparkling house carrying a folding chair in one hand and a paper bag of food in the other. "I don't want to disturb you," he said, "so if it's all right, I'll manage by myself," and set off down the hall to the locked room. Over his shoulder he told us that tonight he would sleep in our house — i.e., in his room — because his family had guests who were using his room, and would we please wake him up at seven, because he had a lot of work to do the next day.

If truth be told, I was a little angry at Abdul Abu Azizi — but I was more afraid, because his son went into the room carrying a bag of food.

Half an hour later, Fa'iz came out of his room and walked confidently to the bathroom. I said in a low voice, "This is impossible. I have to do something. This *goy* walks around our house and is now washing his hands — hands that held chametz! — and who knows where the crumbs will be scattered?"

*Half an hour later, Fa'iz came out of his room and walked
confidently to the bathroom.*

We waited until Fa'iz was back in his room, and then my brother, who was visiting us for Pesach, said, "Look here, you can't keep him from using the room, but he has no right to walk all around and use your facilities."

We finished the Seder without any more interruptions, and the night passed quietly. At seven o'clock in the morning, Fa'iz left noisily. Then I went to speak with Abu Azizi, who greeted me warmly. "You see," he said, "a person doesn't lose when he does someone a favor. As it happened, we had guests last night, and your room was a big help."

"Yes," I stammered, "that's what I wanted to talk to you about. It's all right, but... how can I explain it to you? Fa'iz's walking around the apartment is a problem, I — it's not that I have anything against him, but..."

"What? Are you joking?" interrupted Abu Azizi. "How can he get into the room without going through the apartment? You know what? I see that you're sorry you made the deal, so let's forget about it. Give me back the shekel and everyone will be happy."

"No, no!" I exclaimed, trembling at the thought. "I'm perfectly satisfied. The room is completely yours for all of Pesach. What I'm trying to explain is that there are religious problems about walking around the rest of the apartment, but the room — it's entirely yours."

Abu Azizi said, "I understand. There's a problem. I understand." Then his eyes lit up. "No, there is no problem — there is a solution! The room has a window, right? I will hang a rope ladder from the window and we're done. We'll come in from outside and jump into the room. In this way I'll have no problems and you won't either."

I sighed and nodded in agreement, thanking Abu Azizi.

Three days passed, during which a rope ladder dangled to the ground from a window of our second floor apartment. All this time, suspicious figures climbed up and down and went in and out. It was Fa'iz, his friends, and the rest of his family. Finally, toward the end of the holiday, Mrs. Klepholtz, who lived in the apartment below us, and who had been visiting her children until then, called the police because she was afraid — and for good reason: perhaps the Arabs who climbed in during the evenings and at night would go into her house as well. Therefore, the police demanded that the rope ladder be taken away.

Then I got scared that Abu Azizi would cancel our agreement, or again demand the right to go through our apartment. But he was a good neighbor and said, "Don't worry, it's no big deal. I won't cancel the agreement and I won't give the key to Fa'iz's creepy friends." I thanked him profusely.

Right after Pesach ended, Abu Azizi came to my house and returned the key, and also offered me a pita, "Because," in his words, "it is already permissible for you to eat chametz."

I thanked him, but politely refused his generous offer. I wanted to give him a respectable sum of money for having gotten involved in all of this, but he refused, saying, "I respect the Jews, and also their religion — and besides that, my grandmother was Jewish."

I leapt up as if I had been bitten by a snake and asked carefully what he meant, and it became clear to me that Abu Azizi's mother's mother was Jewish (but had intermarried), which meant that Abu Azizi himself was Jewish… which meant that I had sold my chametz to a Jew…

I ran to the rav's house and in one rush of words told him the whole story: how I remembered almost too late that I had not sold my chametz, how I sold it to Abu Azizi at the last minute, how much anxiety and *agmas nefesh* I had suffered because Abu Azizi's son and his friends came and went in my house during the entire week-long holiday, and how I had just found out that Abu Azizi was Jewish. When I recalled that, I burst into tears and sobbed bitterly. "And after all that I suffered, there was chametz in my house, and who knows if I sold it properly! It may have belonged to me!" The rav sat for a moment and then rebuked me quietly, saying, "You certainly did not transgress any Torah law, for you annulled your chametz; for you it was like the dust of the earth. So stop crying for yourself. The one you should be crying for is our brother, Abu Azizi."

The rav's rebuke woke me up to the real issue — that of saving a fellow-Jew. And from that day on, my whole family was harnessed in this mission. Of course, the rav and the people from Lev l'Achim and Arachim got involved, and we didn't rest until, with Hashem's help, we persuaded Abu Azizi to believe us that he was a Jew. And you won't believe it, but today Abu Azizi is living as a Jew and keeping Torah and *mitzvos*.

# CHAPTER 10

# A GOD-FEARING GENTILE?

We were learning *parashas Zachor* (at the end of *parashas Ki Seitzei*) and we came to the verse, "…and you were faint and weary; and they did not fear God."[1] Rebbe Mendel told us that, according to the Midrash, Hashem arranged it so that Yehoshua would be the one to lead the battle against Amalek. Why? Because Yehoshua was a descendant of Yosef, and since Yosef said to his brothers, "I fear God"[2] after he had held them prisoner for three days when they went down to Egypt for the first time, it was fitting that, as the Midrash says, "The one who fears God will do battle with the one who does not."

No sooner had Rebbe Mendel finished telling us about the Midrash than Aharon burst out, "I just don't understand that accusation against Amalek! I could understand if the Torah had said that Amalek was cruel, or that he wanted to show the whole world that — God forbid! — Hashem couldn't protect

---

1. *Devarim* 25:18.
2. See *Bereishis* 42:18.

us, or, as Rashi says, that he was willing to suffer as long as he could show that *Am Yisrael* was not the strong nation that the whole world thought it was. But to accuse Amalek of not being God-fearing is like… like… like saying that the Nazis — may there memory be erased — didn't pray with enough *kavanah*."

"Very good!" said Rebbe Mendel, beaming with satisfaction. "The Maggid of Dubno asked this very question, and he answered it with a wonderful parable."

> Once upon a time, there were two brothers in a certain town, one rich and the other poor. The rich brother supported the poor one, providing him with food and even giving his clothes to his brother when they were no longer new.
>
> One day, as he was walking through the town, the rich brother happened to see his poor brother dressed in some of the fine clothes he had sent him. But he was shocked and dismayed to see that his brother was was not wearing them neatly, in a respectable way. Instead, he looked completely unkempt, with his coat open and his undershirt peeking out of his half-unbuttoned shirt.
>
> The wealthy brother called the the poor one over, pointed at his coat and said, "What is this? You should be ashamed of yourself! I send you good clothes, and this is the slovenly way you wear them?"
>
> "What can I do?" answered the poor brother. "The clothes you sent me weren't new. The buttons were loose, and some of them came off. That's why my shirt and jacket are open."
>
> The rich brother was mollified and said, "If that is the case, come with me to a clothing store right now and we'll solve the problem."

The wealthy brother was as good as his word. He took his poor brother to a clothing store and bought him a complete set of clothes. "Now you have no excuse," he said, shaking his finger in warning. "The clothes are all new and the buttons are all tight, and I don't want to see you looking unkempt again!"

The brothers went their separate ways, but not many days passed before the rich brother again saw his poor brother in town with his coat open and his shirt unbuttoned. "What do you have to say this time?" the rich brother asked the other angrily. "Why are you dressed this way again? You are an embarrassment to me!"

The poor brother answered, "My dear brother, you are wealthy and accustomed to elegant and sumptuous clothing, and you are careful to be well-dressed at all times. You will never understand the life of the poor. Poor people and beggars often have no clothing but the rags they wear, and they don't care about how they are dressed. That's the way it is."

The wealthy brother listened in silence and swallowed his criticism. "What my brother said is true," he thought. "I know nothing of the life of the poor. Perhaps this is indeed their custom, to go about disheveled. I will no longer trouble him about the way he dresses. Let him dress as the poor do, and may he be happy."

A year passed peacefully. The wealthy man provided his poor brother with food and clothing. The poor man dressed as he pleased, but the rich brother did not criticize him for dressing sloppily. He now believed that that was the way of the poor — to be unkempt and slovenly. Peace reigned, until… until there was a wedding in the family.

The brothers' nephew, their sister's son, was to be married, and, of course, both uncles, the rich one and the poor one, were invited to the wedding.

During the wedding feast, a small stage was arranged for the jester, who — as was the custom in those days — was to amuse the bride and groom and the guests with a stream of jokes and witty songs.

As it happened, the jester not only told jokes and sang songs, but did imitations of all sorts of people. He first appeared dressed up like a Polish squire and imitated the haughty and insulting way they speak. Then, after disappearing behind a screen for a moment, he appeared dressed as an Arab and began yelling in Arabic. Later, he also, *l'havdil,* dressed and spoke like a learned rabbi for a few minutes. Those were only three of the many different costumes he wore and people he imitated.

At one point in the evening, the jester cried out in a loud voice, "Get out your *tzedakah* money!" and stepped behind the screen. When he reappeared a moment later he was not only dressed like a beggar, in ragged and mismatched clothing, but he stooped and shuffled like a beggar. The guests laughed loudly in pleasure at the jester's perfect imitation of a master beggar.

Were all of the guests laughing? No, there was one who was not. The rich brother was not laughing, but carefully studying the jester. He saw that though the jester's shirt was shabby, it was buttoned from top to bottom and tucked into his trousers. The rich brother was furious. He went over to his brother, grabbed him by the arm, and dragged him to a far corner of the hall.

"Did you see the jester?" he said quietly but angrily. "He

acts exactly like a poor man and a born beggar. But look and see: His shirt is buttoned from top to bottom, and it's tucked neatly into his trousers!"

"So what?" mumbled his brother.

"So what, you ask!" said the rich man in a rage. "You told me that the custom of poor people is to wear their shirts unbuttoned and to otherwise look disheveled. If that were true, the jester here would also be wearing his shirt unbuttoned, and he would appear unkempt and slovenly."

"But…" stammered the poor brother, "you know the jester is not really poor."

"What difference does that make?!" shouted the rich man, no longer able to contain himself. "He wants his imitations to be perfect. And if poor people really were in the habit of wearing their shirts unbuttoned, he would do likewise when he imitates them. But he buttons his shirt and tucks it in even when he is wearing his beggar's costume, and that means that even the poorest people do not degrade themselves by going about with their shirts unbuttoned and their jackets open. And you — you will be very sorry indeed if I ever again see you looking disrespectful in public!"

When Rebbe Mendel had finished he said, "That is the parable. Now, what is its moral?"

We didn't know. We all agreed that it was a good story, but we couldn't see how it was connected to Amalek.

"You don't understand?" asked our rebbe, disappointed. "The wealthy brother in the parable is the Holy One, the King of kings. The Torah says that Amalek did not fear Hashem. And Hashem asks Amalek, 'Why do you not fear Me?'

*"Even the poorest people do not degrade themselves by going about with their shirts unbuttoned and their jackets open!"*

"Whereupon Amalek — who in the parable is the poor brother — answers, 'Since when are gentiles God-fearing? The Jews are God-fearing, but it is not the custom of the gentiles to be God-fearing.' In other words, the poor and beggars in the parable stand for the gentiles in general, and dressing appropriately stands for fear of God.

"But then," continued Rebbe Mendel, "Yosef haTzaddik — who in the parable is the jester — says, 'I fear God,' even though he pretended not to recognize his brothers and acted like an Egyptian in every way. That is just like the jester, who pretends to act like a beggar in every way. Nevertheless, even though Yosef was a 'gentile,' as it were, he said to his brothers, 'I fear God.' He wasn't afraid that because of these words his brothers would figure out that he was not really a gentile — just as the jester wasn't concerned that people would figure out he wasn't really a beggar. This shows… What does this show us?" asked Rebbe Mendel.

"It shows that even gentiles are God-fearing!" Michael said excitedly.

"Exactly!" exclaimed Rebbe Mendel with satisfaction. "And therefore Amalek's defense collapses, and the Amalekites will be punished, not only because of their cruelty to the Jews and their profanation of Hashem's holy Name, but also because they were not God-fearing."

# CHAPTER II

# A TRANSACTION BETWEEN YISSACHAR AND YISSACHAR

Yissachar and Zevulun learned in the same yeshiva. Both were outstanding in both their learning and their diligence, and both wanted to grow in Torah. But there was one difference between them: Whereas Yissachar's desire was only for Torah and he was wont to say, "The greatest Gan Eden is to sit in front of the *shtender* and learn," Zevulun wanted to learn Torah while enjoying wealth and well-being.

Often, the two would argue about this. Yissachar maintained that wealth was a greater trial than poverty — and anyhow, what do you need besides Torah? Whatever Hashem gives, may He be blessed and His name be blessed. And Zevulun said that wealth and property were also important, and they didn't interfere with Torah study but in fact helped, just as Rabbi Yehudah haNasi was wealthy and it didn't interfere with his Torah learning.

In this way the two would argue from time to time, this one maintaining his opinion forcefully and this one maintaining his position forcefully. But they were of one mind that the study of Torah was the most important thing.

Years passed. Yissachar and Zevulun established families and households based on Torah and Torah values. But…

Yissachar sat and learned Torah in poverty and earned his living from the meager allowance he got from the *kollel*, while his wife also worked to support the home. Everyone in the family was happy that Yissachar had made Torah study his "profession."

But while Yissachar sat and enjoyed the glory of Torah and fulfilled the precept, "One increases holiness and does not decrease it"[1] and practiced like Beis Hillel, who constantly "increased the light," Zevulun did like Beis Shammai and "decreased the light."[2] In the beginning, he learned Torah most of the day and worked two hours. Later, he started working half a day. And eventually, he devoted himself entirely to his business, except for a *shiur* in the shul between *Minchah* and *Ma'ariv*.

Success shone on Zevulun. From a subordinate clerk he became a supervisor. After that he became assistant manager. After a time he was appointed department manager. Eventually he left his employer and opened a private office, and his business prospered greatly.

Thus, while Yissachar lived simply and was hard-pressed, Zevulun lived ostentatiously and in the lap of luxury. He gave large sums to *tzedakah* and was very pleased with himself.

---

1. *Berachos* 28a.
2. *Shabbos* 21b, referring to whether we add a Chanukah light each day of Chanukah, or start with eight and decrease each night.

But there came even harder times. Yissachar's wife could not continue working, and his allowance from the *kollel* was cut due to new government legislation. As things developed, it came to the point that there was simply nothing in the house to eat.

Then Yissachar turned to his wife and said, "'It is time to act for Hashem; they have made void Your Torah.'[3] In other words, it is Hashem's will and I have no choice. I must learn Torah less and work part of the day for our livelihood."

Yissachar's wife said to him, "*Chas v'shalom!* You must continue learning full time."

Yissachar said to her, "But what will we do? I do not want to ask for charity, and you cannot work. What will we eat from now on? With what will we feed the children?"

Yissachar's wife answered, "I have an idea; try it, and if it you don't succeed — do as you wish. Surely you remember your friend Zevulun, whom you told me about many times, how you used to learn together — you told me he's wealthy, with property and..."

"Are you suggesting that I ask my friend for charity?" asked Yissachar. "I'm not interested in that."

"*Chalilah*," answered Yissachar's wife. "Do not ask him for any charity, but make a business arrangement with him — an arrangement like that of Yissachar and Zevulun. Did you not tell me that this man Zevulun loves Torah? Surely he will be happy to buy half of your reward for Torah study in return for a few small coins."

---

3. *Tehillim* 119:126.

"An agreement like that of Yissachar and Zevulun? You mean that I should relinquish half the reward of my Torah study?"

"And why not?" answered Yissachar's wife. "If you don't get some help, you will anyway have to toil half a day for your livelihood — so either way you'll lose half the reward of the Torah."

With a heavy heart Yissachar agreed to his wife's proposal. He called his friend Zevulun to make an appointment to see him and, filled with shame, went to his house.

When Zevulun saw Yissachar, he ran to him and hugged him and brought him into his luxurious living room and said, "How wonderful it is to see you again! There were many times that I wanted to visit you, but you are in the *beis midrash* all day. Do you remember how much the two of us took pleasure in learning Torah?"

"I remember very well," said Yissachar. "Please tell me, dear friend, don't you yearn for the *shtender?* It is hard for me to understand how you left behind — but what am I saying? Did I come here to admonish you?"

"I also think," said Zevulun, "that it is a pity I don't learn Torah anymore. But what can I do? My business affairs are many, and with God's help I will marry off my children comfortably, and they will be able to sit and learn Torah."

Zevulun sighed and continued, "But you said you came to ask a favor of me. What is it? I will be happy to help you if I can."

"I want to propose a Yissachar-Zevulun agreement," said Yissachar quickly, lowering his eyes.

"A Yissachar-Zevulun agreement?" exclaimed Zevulun in

*"Don't you yearn for the shtender, my dear friend?"*

surprise. "You mean that you will learn Torah and I will support you?"

Yissachar gathered his courage and said, "You won't support me. You will make a good deal. Half of my merit for Torah study will be yours, and as for me, I will not ask for much money. I will be satisfied with just a little."

"But what are you talking about? What kind of an arrangement is that? Even if you will be satisfied with almost nothing, I will have to pay you at least four thousand shekels a month, which is forty-eight thousand shekels a year, which is almost half a million shekels in ten years…"

"Which is thousands of hours of Torah study and thousands of pages of Gemara that will be recorded to your credit," answered Yissachar.

Zevulun chuckled and said, "Do you really think that this is a profitable arrangement for me?"

"Can there be any doubt?" asked Yissachar, amazed. "I am shocked to hear you making light of it. But if you aren't interested, I won't waste any more of your time."

"Just a minute!" exclaimed Zevulun. "Do you truly and honestly believe that this is a profitable arrangement for me, to be your 'Zevulun'?"

"Certainly, certainly!" answered Yissachar.

"If so," exclaimed Zevulun triumphantly, "I will give you a little test. Instead of my being your 'Zevulun,' you will be *my* 'Zevulun'!"

"What do you mean?" asked Yissachar.

"Well, I assume that you will have to work half a day if I don't agree to support you," explained Zevulun. "If so, divide your earnings in two — take half to support yourself and your family, and give the other half to me, and I will learn two hours a day."

"But you are a wealthy man, and even if you learn for two hours every day, it won't decrease your livelihood," asserted Yissachar.

"True," said Zevulun, "but you know that my heart is drawn to business! And besides that, I want to see if it's true, as you said, that it pays to be a 'Zevulun.' Therefore, I say: I am not prepared under any circumstances to be your 'Zevulun,' but I propose that you be my 'Zevulun,' in return for two hours that I will set aside for learning Torah."

Yissachar closed his eyes and furrowed his brow. After a moment he said, "I agree!"

"What?" said Zevulun, incredulous. "You mean that seriously? You're actually prepared not only to lose half a day of your learning, but also to make do with half your earnings?"

"Yes," answered Yissachar, "but as you said, I will be your 'Zevulun,' and thus will have the merit of half your Torah study. So bring a pen and paper, and let's write out the details of our agreement."

Zevulun bit his lip. He had made a deal and didn't know how to get out of it. In his heart of hearts he had no desire at all to sit and learn two hours a day, and he also wasn't in need of Yissachar's meager money. The whole proposal was a joke, in order to defeat Yissachar's proposition — but now he couldn't back down.

"All right," he sighed. He opened a drawer and took out a pen and paper, wrote out the particulars of the agreement twice, and invited his friend to co-sign each copy.

"I wrote that the arrangement is for one year," explained

Zevulun. "It may be that after a year you won't want to continue with it."

"Excellent!" said Yissachar, and a smile appeared on his face. It was obvious that he felt great satisfaction.

"You really are happy?" asked Zevulun doubtfully.

"Truly and perfectly!" said Yissachar. "It's not every day that a mitzvah like this comes my way, to be the 'Zevulun' of a Zevulun like you."

The two friends separated, and Yissachar returned to his house happy and in good spirits.

"From the look on your face," said Yissachar's wife, "I see that you succeeded in making a Yissachar-Zevulun arrangement."

"Indeed!" said Yissachar, and he spoke to his wife of the agreement which he had signed.

Yissachar's wife's mouth fell open when she heard that her husband was going to have to abandon his learning for half a day, but she said nothing. Indeed, she had promised her husband that if Zevulun refused to support them, Yissachar could do as he pleased.

In the meantime, Yissachar looked for part-time work. He hoped to find something in the Torah world, which would also pay enough to support his family on only half the wages.

"He who comes to purify himself is helped by Heaven."[4] Yissachar found work in a religious institution for the blind. It was his job to transcribe *mishnayos* into Braille. Since he had to work, he was grateful that he had found a job that helped

---

4. *Shabbos* 104a.

make Torah accessible to the blind — and he was thrilled to be able to learn while working as well.

Zevulun knew he had to keep his part of the agreement, but he hoped that within a few days Yissachar would come to him and ask to cancel. Truth be told, he was surprised at Yissachar. He thought, "Not only to labor half a day, but also to lose half the wages?"

But the bottom line was that Zevulun had no intention of taking any of Yissachar's meager wages. For the time being, however, he did not want to reveal this for two reasons. First, in order to see whether Yissachar would indeed keep his word, and second — so he hoped — that because of his great poverty, Yissachar would be forced to cancel the agreement. Then he, Zevulun, would be released from the burden of the two "oppressive" hours of Torah study.

Be that as it may, Zevulun turned to his bookcase, wondering which *sefer* to take. In the end, his hand rested on *maseches Bava Kamma*. He sat down and began to learn. At first he felt strange as he read the words he had left behind twenty years before, but after a few minutes he was immersed in the *sugya*. Questions and answers that he had learned in yeshiva rose in his memory, and while he was thus engaged he heard the voice of his wife calling him.

"I can't stop now," he answered her. "You know I undertook to learn two hours a day."

"I know. But two and a half hours have already passed," she answered.

Zevulun was astonished. "Two and a half hours? I didn't even notice," he said, and a feeling of great satisfaction filled his heart.

After a few days, Zevulun decided that instead of sitting at home and learning by himself, it would be better to go to the *kollel* where his friend Yissachar learned. "If I am giving two hours to it, then they should be two hours of *geshmak*," he thought to himself.

But when he got to the *kollel* the next afternoon, he was told that Yissachar came only in the morning.

"Ah," remembered Zevulun, "of course! In the afternoon he needs to work."

The next morning, Zevulun informed the people in his office that starting the next day he would come to the office only at eleven o'clock. And by nine o'clock the following morning, he was already leaning over a *shtender* in the *kollel*.

When Yissachar arrived a few minutes later, Zevulun got up and walked quickly toward him. "*Baruch ha-ba!*" he greeted his friend. "I've been longing to ask you if you remember the *peshat* of Rav Chayim on the Tosafos in the matter of *shor ha-mazik*, an ox that causes damage."

A few minutes later, the two were bent over a table, and piles of books were open before them.

Months passed. Zevulun would come to the *kollel* every day to learn *b'chavrusa* with Yissachar for two hours, and at the end of every month, Yissachar would bring him two thousand shekels.

"*Ziel sh'kol lenafshach* — go take it for yourself from you," Zevulun would say in Aramaic every time. "I should steal what little money you have?"

But Yissachar would press the money into his hand, saying, "An agreement is an agreement." Zevulun would shrug his shoulders and put the money away in a drawer.

After several months of learning, Yissachar felt that Zevulun was catching up to him, asking difficult questions and answering others.

"This is so wonderful!" exclaimed Yissachar in admiration. "You are now just as you were in yeshiva. Besides that, you remember every word of the *shiurim* that we heard twenty years ago — and you tell it over in an interesting and refreshing way."

"Something one enjoys, one remembers well," answered Zevulun, sighing with satisfaction. "And to think that one even gets a reward in Heaven for this pleasure."

"Absolutely," replied Yissachar. "And I am particularly happy about the reward that I shall get, as your 'Zevulun,' from your wonderful learning."

At that moment, Zevulun bit his lip and said, "What a fool I was! Such wonderful learning, and its priceless reward I sell in return for two thousand shekels that I don't even need."

Yissachar didn't say a word in reply, and the two continued their learning.

That evening, Zevulun came to Yissachar's modest home. "To what do I owe the honor of your visit?" asked Yissachar.

Zevulun sighed and turned to Yissachar. "I am sure you remember that about six months ago, you came to me and asked me to be your 'Zevulun.' Not only did I scoff and refuse, but you became my 'Zevulun.' Now I have a request to make of you."

"What is your request?" asked Yissachar, although he had a fair idea of what Zevulun's request would be.

"It's like this," said Zevulun. "I think I made a bad deal when I agreed that you would get half the credit for my learning. It's hard for me think that I, who learn only two hours a day, am giving up half the reward that I will get in Heaven. This upsets me to no end. So I came here tonight in order to ask you to cancel the agreement. Stop being my 'Zevulun' and leave me the whole reward for learning."

"Did you really think I would cancel the agreement?" said Yissachar tenderly but firmly. "How can I relinquish the reward of even an hour of Torah learning? After all, it is more precious than gold." (The reader should not think Yissachar's refusal cruel. He had a reason for his actions, as will be seen below.)

"Please," begged Zevulun, "hear my proposal: I am prepared to grant your original request. Sit and learn Torah all day, and I will be your 'Zevulun' — provided that you leave me the two hours, which will be entirely mine."

"Even if I accept your proposal, I can't start immediately," answered Yissachar, "since I promised to give the place where I work a month's notice before I leave. And even if they let me leave immediately, I'm not sure if I'm willing to give up my right to be your 'Zevulun.'"

"But why?" asked Zevulun. "After all, if you accept my offer, you will be able to sit and learn the entire day, and you will gain much more than what you're taking from me."

"Leave that to me, and don't be angry with me," answered Yissachar. "But an agreement is an agreement. At the end of the year, you'll be able to cancel it, as we agreed."

"All right," answered a downcast Zevulun, and he got ready to leave Yissachar's house.

"Wait a minute!" Yissachar stopped him. "I have a suggestion for you, by means of which you will be able to get the reward of two full hours of learning: Learn for three hours, and then, even though the reward for one hour will be mine — you'll be left with two whole hours that belong just to you."

"I'll think about it," answered Zevulun, walking to the door.

Yissachar accompanied him and said, "Don't be angry with me, Zevulun. What we're talking about is a priceless reward."

"I am not angry at you, but at myself. I should have agreed to be your 'Zevulun' from the outset."

"Don't feel bad about it," answered Yissachar. "After all, because of our agreement you learn two whole hours every day. And if you accept my suggestion, you will be able to learn three — or even four — hours a day."

Zevulun left Yissachar's house and did a *cheshbon hanefesh*. He also took stock of his wealth, and found that even if he came to his office for only half a day, he wouldn't be any poorer. He discussed the matter with his wife.

"If you were to listen to me," said Zevulun's wife, "you would do as your friend advises. You can't imagine how much things have changed since you started to learn. I don't know how, but the whole house has become imbued with a *Torani* atmosphere. Our children — who previously cared only about having fun — have changed. Their words are more thoughtful and they are more refined. I would go as far as to say that it would be worthwhile for you to sit and learn the whole day."

"The whole day? What are you talking about? Who will manage my affairs?" asked Zevulun in surprise.

"Your affairs prosper by themselves," replied Zevulun's wife. "You yourself once said to me, 'Even if I were to sit in the office and do nothing, my wealth would continue to grow.' I didn't understand what you meant, but this is how you expressed yourself."

"There is some truth in what you are saying," replied Zevulun, "but for now, I will learn half a day in the *kollel*, and will go to the office only in the afternoon."

After two months, Zevulun was an *avreich* in every way. He was immersed in the Gemara, and his business was his secondary occupation.

One day, as they were leaving the *kollel*, Zevulun said to Yissachar, "I thank you for your wonderful advice, and I am requesting again: Please, let me have back the hour of reward that is in the agreement. I'll make it worth your while. I will pay your entire salary, and you will be able to sit and learn undisturbed. I do not even ask to make an agreement like Yissachar and Zevulun; all the reward for the learning will be yours."

"I'll think about it," promised Yissachar.

The next day Yissachar arrived at the *kollel* and said to Zevulun, "I am willing to cancel the original agreement on one condition."

"And that is?" asked Zevulun expectantly.

"That you are obliged to come to the *kollel* for the whole day," answered Yissachar dramatically.

"And who will look after my affairs?" asked Zevulun in amazement.

"Leave your business be," replied Yissachar pleasantly. "Tell me, you have money to live on?"

"Thank God, I have money to live on for the rest of my life, and with God's help also enough to marry off my children respectably. But..."

"But — what?" asked Yissachar. "Why should you further enlarge this capital?" Come back to us! Return completely to our ranks!"

Zevulun paced back and forth. It was obvious that deep in his heart a battle was raging. In the end he said to Yissachar, "You have defeated me. I accept your proposal to learn for a whole day — but I also have one condition."

"And what is it?" asked Yissachar.

"That you too sit the whole day in *kollel,* and I support you. In that way you will be able to learn in peace and tranquility."

And thus, dear reader, both men turned into Yissachars, which they still are today.

## CHAPTER 12

# A STORY ABOUT HALF A HAIRCUT

We heard this story when we were learning the laws pertaining to the seven-week period of Sefiras haOmer. Rebbe Mendel explained to us the various approaches regarding having one's hair cut during this time. Among them was the approach of those who are strict and do not cut their hair at all during these seven weeks, except on Rosh Chodesh Iyar and Lag baOmer, and from Rosh Chodesh Sivan until Shavuos.

Rebbe Mendel wanted to continue with his words, when Asher asked in surprise, "And they cut hair on Rosh Chodesh Iyar and Rosh Chodesh Sivan?"

"Yes," said Rebbe Mendel with a smile. "I think I know what you want to ask — but ask it yourself."

Asher said, "I thought you taught us, Rebbe, that it is forbidden to have one's hair cut on Rosh Chodesh at all, without any connection to Sefiras haOmer."

"Well," said Rebbe Mendel, "not exactly. Rabbi Yehudah heChasid wrote in his will that one should not cut his hair — or even his fingernails — on Rosh Chodesh, but there are those who say that he only meant this for his descendants and not for anyone else."

"And what is the rebbe's practice?" asked Rafi.

"My custom is to follow Rabbi Yehudah heChasid's will and not cut my hair or nails on Rosh Chodesh," answered Rebbe Mendel.

Silence prevailed for a moment, and then Rebbe Mendel said, "That reminds me of the business with Elimelech the barber — and don't ask me to tell you about it, because I will, without your asking."

*One time when I went into the barbershop, I saw that it was empty (except for the barber). This made me happy, because it meant that I wouldn't have to wait before getting my hair cut. No sooner had I settled down comfortably in the barber's chair than two men walked in together. From their conversation, I understood that neither of them was sure who should go first after me. At any rate, I could see that the two were in a big hurry.*

*"Please give me the same haircut you gave me last time," I said to Elimelech. He nodded, and then brought that frightening-looking electric shaver close to my neck and began to shave the back of my head on the right side. He had just started when a third person came into the barbershop, and said warmly to everyone, "Chodesh tov! Have a good and blessed month!"*

*"Chodesh tov," I began to answer, and suddenly felt the blood draining from my face. "Oy vey — how could I have forgotten? Today is Rosh Chodesh!"*

*"Nu, so what of it?" asked the barber, and he turned to resume his work on my head, this time on the left side.*

*"Stop!" I cried. "Don't clip any more! Today is Rosh Chodesh, and I don't cut my hair on Rosh Chodesh."*

"Oh, thank you!" exclaimed the two gentlemen who were in a hurry. "I forgot entirely," said one, and the other nodded and added, "Of course; Rabbi Yehudah heChasid!" The two of them put on their hats and quickly left the barbershop.

"What's the matter?" asked the third man (the one who, to his merit, had reminded me that today was Rosh Chodesh).

"What's the matter? It's very simple," I answered as I took off the bar-ber's sheet. "Rabbi Yehudah heChasid wrote in his will that one shouldn't have his hair cut on Rosh Chodesh — some even say it's dangerous to do so — and I thank you for reminding me that today is Rosh Chodesh."

"Oh, I didn't know that," said the man. "I don't know what my custom is, but still, why should I do it? I'll get my hair cut some other time." And he walked out of the shop while Elimelech, who had stood silently holding the buzzing clipper in his hand since I told him to stop cutting my hair, stared at him in amazement.

After he had left the shop, Elimelech turned to me and said furiously, "Robber! Bandit that you are! You've managed to empty out my whole shop. Who gave you the right? I know perfectly well that there are many people who do get their hair cut on Rosh Chodesh! Who put you in charge? You have stolen a hundred shekels from me — twenty-five times four! Next time, think before you speak!"

Now the color of my face changed from pale white to deep red on account of the rain of insults that fell on me — but with Hashem's help I controlled my stormy emotions and said to Elimelech in the mildest tone I could muster, "Please forgive me. You are right. Maybe I shouldn't have spoken. But let us see if you really suffered a loss. Isn't it true that those men will come back to have their hair cut here? In any case, I assure you that tomorrow, or even maybe this evening, I will come back to have my hair cut, and I am willing to pay in advance."

Elimelech seemed a little embarrassed by his outburst and said, "Let's see: You said you would come to get your hair cut, and Mr. Kloyzenbach (the one who came in last) will also come back; he's a regular customer. But the other men — I don't recognize them, and I earn twenty-five shekels for each head — so it may be that I have lost fifty shekels. Nu, that's not so terrible. Kapparah!"

"No, absolutely not," I said. "I will pay you the fifty shekels."

"You don't have to," he said. "You know what? Give me twenty-five. We'll split the damage, and if those two return, I'll give you your money back."

I took out fifty shekels and put it in the barber's hand.

"Why fifty?" the barber asked. "We agreed on twenty-five."

"Yes," I answered, "but there's another twenty-five for my haircut. I told you I would pay in advance."

"Fine," said Elimelech as he put the money in his pocket. I started to leave, but he suddenly grabbed my shoulder and turned me around so he could see the back of my head. "Wait a minute," he said. "There's still a problem here."

"What's the problem?" I asked.

"The problem is your head," said the barber, and quickly explained, "that is, I didn't mean your mind — I meant the outside of your head. Look!" he ordered, shoving a mirror into my hand.

Behind me was the big mirror of the barbershop, and when I looked in the mirror that the barber had given me, I saw my back reflected in the big mirror. Now I understood what the problem was. Half of the back of my head was shaved, and the other half was full of hair.

"Nu," asked the barber, "what do you say? What should we do?"

"It's not so terrible," I said. "After all, I'm coming back tomorrow morning, and then my whole head will be shaved."

"And in the meantime? Everyone will stare at you."

"Nonsense," I said, waving my hand in dismissal. "Who pays attention? It's all right." I tried to leave the barbershop, but Elimelech stopped me.

"No, it's not all right!" he cried. "People will see you in the street and will say, 'That's the way Elimelech the barber cuts hair? I won't come to his barbershop anymore.'"

"Don't worry," I said to the barber, "I'll turn up my jacket collar and run home."

"And what about after that, in shul?" the barber asked in a worried voice. "Do me a favor, Reb Mendel. Let me at least finish shaving the back of your head."

"Absolutely not!" I protested loudly.

"Maybe in this case it's permitted? Maybe you should call your rav."

"No," I said. "I know there are those who permit it, but I am very careful about this. And you don't have to worry so much — how will people know where I got my hair cut?"

"I'll forget abut the money — I won't charge you, just let me cut your hair," pleaded the barber.

"No," I had to insist.

"Then do me a favor and wait here until the evening, and then I'll cut your hair."

I began to think about the barber's proposal. I had already prayed Minchah, so maybe I could wait in the barbershop until evening. But then I remembered that I had told my family that I would be home by five-thirty. Our argument continued until, with Hashem's help, the two sides reached a peace agreement.

"What was the agreement?" someone called out while we all waited.

"The agreement," said Rebbe Mendel, "was this. I called a cab (the telephone call was at the barber's expense, but I paid for the cab), and when it arrived I turned up the collar of my jacket and ran to the cab, with Elimelech running after me to hide what had been done to my neck. The cab took me straight home, and there I ran quickly into my apartment (after I paid,

*I turned up the collar of my jacket and ran to the cab.*

of course), where I remained confined until eight o'clock in the evening. And then Elimelech appeared at my door with all his equipment, including a sheet and a mirror, and cut my hair carefully. Afterwards I paid him (according to the agreement) a bonus of fifty shekels for his house call. After that I was permitted to leave and daven *Ma'ariv*."

"Oy! That was an expensive business," said Moishie.

"Indeed," chuckled Rebbe Mendel, "but wouldn't you know? Elimelech checked things out and discovered that he was a descendant of Rabbi Yehudah heChasid! He was so grateful to me for making him aware of his famous ancestor's will that he returned all my money and now gives me free haircuts — except on Rosh Chodesh, of course."

# CHAPTER 13

# *THE WOODEN WAGON*

I t was a few days before Lag baOmer and it was very hot. We were having a hard time concentrating. Suddenly, Rebbe Mendel sighed, gave us look, and said, "I would like to tell you a story within a story within a story," and without further ado began.

*The first story took place when I was a pupil in sixth grade, during the few days before Lag baOmer and on Lag baOmer itself.*

*Like Jewish children everywhere, we wanted our bonfire to be big and high. To that end, we collected as much wood as we could. Every boy in the class gathered wood. The closer it got to Lag baOmer, the more effort each boy put into the project. I, too, was involved. I devoted an hour every day to gathering wood in every form I could find, including old packing crates and pieces of tree trunks.*

*One day when I was — with great difficulty — dragging a tree trunk whose length was nearly three times my height, I spied a large wooden wagon in Yaakobovitch's yard. It was the wagon that he had used for his deliveries in the days when he was a milkman.*

Rebbe Mendel paused in his tale to explain that once upon a time people did not buy milk in the grocery store or supermarket. Each family had a milkman, and the milkman delivered milk to his customers with his wagon or truck. Milk came in glass bottles in those days, Rebbe Mendel told us, but after a time the glass bottles were replaced by plastic bags, the milkmen lost their jobs, and milk was delivered only to grocery stores and supermarkets.

"So at the time of this story," continued Rebbe Mendel, "Yaakobovitch was no longer a milkman. Nevertheless, he kept his wooden wagon. Maybe he thought that some day he would go back to his old job."

*Anyhow, when I saw the wagon, I thought that if Yaakobovitch would let me use it, I could gather a lot of wood with very little effort. So I put down the tree trunk I had been dragging and went and knocked on the former milkman's door. When he opened it, I asked him if I could please borrow his wagon to carry wood for our Lag baOmer bonfire.*

*"You want to borrow my wagon, yingeleh? asked Yaakobovitch. "To collect wood? That's nice! When I was your age, in the little town of Zlotshov, I, too, gathered wood for the Lag baOmer bonfire. I remember it as if it were yesterday. You promise to take good care of the wagon? Fine! Take it, but don't forget that you are responsible for it."*

*I thanked Yaakobovitch and promised him that, b'ezras Hashem, I would be very careful with his wagon and would return it to him on the day of Lag baOmer, the morning after the bonfires.*

*I will skip now to the evening of Lag baOmer without describing at length how hard we worked gathering wood. As Meir was getting ready to light the bonfire, I looked again with satisfaction at the tower we had built so carefully with the wood we had collected, then at the blazing torch that Meir was holding… But when I glanced at the place where I had "parked" Yaakobovitch's wagon half an hour before, I didn't see it!*

*"Meir!" I yelled, "Stop! Yaakobovitch's wagon has disappeared!"*

*"You want to borrow my wagon, yingeleh?"*

The whole class gathered around me. "Yaakobovitch's wagon isn't where I left it. Did someone think that it was meant for the bonfire, too? So wait, don't light the fire. I want to see if the wagon is somewhere in the pile." It was already quite dark, so we turned on our flashlights and carefully examined the tower of wood, but… No! The wagon wasn't there.

"What will I do now?" I wailed. "I have to find the wagon! I promised Yaakobovitch…"

"Calm down," said Shraga, one of the leaders of the class. He took the torch from Meir, extinguished the flame, and announced that the bonfire lighting would be postponed for half an hour so that everyone could help me find the wagon.

After a quarter of an hour in which it seemed we searched everywhere, I promised myself, bli neder, that if the missing wagon turned up, I would learn all of Mishnah Yoma by heart before Shavuos.

I hadn't finished making that silent promise when my younger brother came running up to me, puffing and panting.

"I heard that you're looking for the wagon," he said between breaths. "Stop worrying. I returned it to Yaakobovitch right after you left it by the bonfire."

"Why didn't you tell me?" I asked angrily. "My friends are all running around looking for it and we even postponed lighting the bonfire. And all because of you!"

"Why are you angry?" cried my brother aggrievedly. "I was just trying to help you. I saw the wagon near the bonfire and I was afraid that someone would add it to the pile. I meant to tell you, but I didn't see you. What's important is that the wagon is safe in Yaakobovitch's yard. I don't understand why, instead of thanking me, you're mad at me."

And so, finally, we lit our great tower of scrap lumber, and we "rejoiced and exulted." But that isn't the end of the story.

Later that evening I remembered that I had taken it upon myself to learn Mishnah Yoma if the missing wagon were found, and it occurred to *me that I might actually not be obligated to do it. Don't misunderstand me — it's not that I didn't want to fulfill my promise, but that I was curious about what the halachah is in such a case.*

"One minute," Yedidyah interrupted. "Why did the rebbe think that he was not obligated to fulfill the promise?"

Rebbe Mendel answered, "Let me explain. You see, when I promised to learn all the *mishnayos* in *maseches Yoma* if the wagon was found, I was really no longer in trouble. I made the promise because I thought the wagon was lost. However, because it wasn't lost when I made the promise and actually had never been lost, I thought it was possible that I didn't have to keep the promise. That's what occurred to me."

Rebbe Mendel immediately added, "Don't worry! I did learn Mishnah *Yoma* by heart, but you will learn from the story I am about to tell you that the question is not so simple."

*The next day I went to a rav who lived nearby and asked whether I could ask him a halachic question. The rav welcomed me warmly and asked me to sit down. He listened attentively to my story, and when I was finished said with a smile, "Your reason for thinking that you may not be obligated is a very good one. Let me tell you about a din Torah in the days of the Maharsham that arose because of this very opinion." [To the dear reader: Rav Shalom Mordechai haKohen Schwadron, or "the Maharsham" — the grandfather of Rav Shlomo Schwadron z"tl — was one of the greatest of the poskim of his time. He lived about one hundred and fifty years ago.]*

*"And so," said the rav, "this is what happened: A regiment of the king's army made its camp outside a certain town. The soldiers — non-Jews, of course — sat there for days with nothing to do, for their commander was waiting for a message with orders for the regiment from army headquarters*

in the capital city. But no message came. The soldiers were getting tired of waiting. Every day they became more bored and restless, until finally one day they burst into the town, running wild, plundering stores, and getting drunk on wine stolen from the town's wine merchants. Needless to say, when the soldiers were drunk they were even wilder, and the people of the town, especially the Jews, suffered greatly from them.

"The town's non-Jewish inhabitants did nothing, for they believed there was nothing they could do. They merely consoled themselves with the thought that the regiment would be moving on very soon. But the Jews, after the soldiers had robbed and rioted for several days and there was no sign that they were about to leave, decided to turn for help to a wonder-working tzaddik who lived in a nearby town. Accordingly, they sent a delegation of community dignitaries to appeal to him for help.

"After the leader of the delegation had described the Jews' plight, the tzaddik said that he would take it upon himself to pray that their affliction would be lifted and the soldiers would go away — provided that they contribute a very large sum of money, thousands of gold coins, for the sustenance of orphans and widows.

"The dignitaries of the afflicted community decided that the presence of the soldiers had become pikuach nefesh, and that therefore they must do everything in their power to rid the town of the regiment. Accordingly, they collected the sum the tzaddik had demanded and brought it to him the very next day. He immediately sent the money to where it had to go, and blessed the people of the town, saying that God would help them and that they would quickly be rid of the soldiers.

"The delegation set out for home. When they reached their town they were greeted with good news: A messenger from the army, carrying orders for the regiment to move on, had galloped up a few hours before, and the soldiers were breaking camp.

"After discussing this development, the leaders of the community came to the conclusion that since the order to leave had just arrived, and since *it takes three days on a fast horse to get from the capital to the town, the messenger must have set out on his journey three days before — that is, he was already on his way when they decided to give the tzaddik the money he had demanded. 'If we had known that the messenger was on his way,' one of them said, 'we would never have agreed to donate such an enormous sum. Therefore, our decision concerning the donation was misguided, and our agreement is like a mekach ta'us — a purchase made in error!' The other dignitaries agreed, so they immediately set out again for the nearby town where the wonder-working tzaddik lived.*

*"'Honored rav,' said the leader of the delegation, 'we have good news for you. No sooner had we reached our town than we were told that a messenger had arrived on horseback not long before with orders for the regiment to move on. We thank you for your blessing and your prayers, but … we think we ought to get our money back, because when we gave it to you we did not know that the army messenger was already on his way.' The tzaddik — who, as we know, had already distributed the money to needy widows and orphans — did not accept the argument of the community dignitaries. Therefore, both sides decided to take the case to the great posek, the Maharsham.*

*"When they came before the Maharsham, the representatives of the community explained the circumstances and then argued that they should get the money back, saying, 'After all, we agreed to donate the astronomical sum the tzaddik demanded only so that in the merit of our giving tzedakah the soldiers would leave. But now it is clear that it was not our tzedakah that removed the affliction, because the order for the regiment to move was given even before we gave the tzedakah.'*

*"To this, the tzaddik to whom they had given the money replied, saying, 'It certainly is possible that the merit of your giving tzedakah caused the troops to be ordered to leave — even though the order was issued before you gave the money.'*

*"After hearing the arguments of both sides, the Maharsham decreed*

*that the Jews of the town were not entitled to get their money back. 'Justice is on the side of the rav to whom you turned,' he said to the representatives of the community. 'It is certainly possible that because of the merit of a deed that he will do in the future, a man will be saved from some trouble or affliction before the deed is done, for surely the Holy One knows if the man will or will not do it. Therefore, because you are not able to prove that it was not your tzedakah that saved you, the money does not have to be returned to you.'*

*"After he gave his decision, the Maharsham said, 'There is clear proof from the prophets that a good deed that someone did helped him even before he did the deed. Surely you are familiar with the story at the end of the haftarah for parashas Shemini, which tells about the bringing of the Aron Bris Hashem to Yerushalayim..."*

"Ahh," interrupted Shlomi, "now I understand what the rebbe meant when he said that this was a story within a story within a story. First, the story about the wooden wagon, after that the story about the Maharsham, and now the story about bringing the *Aron* to Yerushalayim."

"Indeed," said Rebbe Mendel, smiling. "Now I will tell you briefly what is told in the *haftarah* of *Shemini*, even though I hope that you all remember it — for not much time has passed since that *parashah*.

"After the *Pelishtim* destroyed the *Mishkan* at Shilo and carried off the *Aron Bris Hashem*, Hashem smote them with terrible sicknesses. The wise men of the *Pelishtim* then took counsel and decided to send the *Aron* back to its place. They took a wagon and hitched two cows to it, and put the *Aron* on the wagon. After that, the *Aron* was in Kiryas Yearim for twenty years, until King David decided to take it up to Yerushalayim. Do you know what comes next, Sa'adiah?" asked Rebbe Mendel.

"Yes," replied Sa'adiah. "They put the *Aron Bris Hashem* on a wagon and Uzza and Achio, the sons of Avinadav, drove the cart in the direction of Yerushalayim. But in the middle of the journey, Uzza saw that the *Aron* was moving from its place and he was afraid that it would fall. He put out his hand to hold the *Aron* and died instantly."

"Correct," said Rebbe Mendel. "And how does the story continue, Asher?"

"King David," said Asher, "was afraid to take the *Aron* up to Yerushalayim, and therefore left it in the house of Oved Edom haGitti (who was a Levi). Three months later, when King David saw that Hashem had blessed the house of Oved Edom haGitti, he realized that he could take the *Aron* up to Yerushalayim."

"Very good!" said Rebbe Mendel. "And now I will tell you what the Gemara at the end of *maseches Berachos* says about this. The Gemara says that because Oved Edom haGitti honored the *Aron Bris Hashem*, his wife and each of his eight daughters-in-law gave birth to six children at one time — that is, fifty-four descendants all together.

"Now," said Rebbe Mendel, "we will go back to the Maharsham, who turned to the residents of the town and said to them: 'King David understood that because of the honor that Oved Edom haGitti gave to the *Aron*, Hashem caused nine women of one family to have six babies each. But the *Aron Bris Hashem* was in the house of Oved Edom haGitti only three months. Therefore, the great miracle of "six in one belly" had been prepared six months before the *Aron* was brought to Oved's house. From this we see that it is certainly possible that because of a good deed that a person will do only way in the future, Hashem sends him blessings now. Likewise, in your case, justice is with the *tzaddik*, not with you, because it is certainly possible that the messenger set out only because of the merit of the *tzedakah* that you gave long afterwards.'"

Rebbe Mendel paused and then continued, "I was told this whole story — about the *psak* of the Maharsham and the proof that he brought from King David — by the rav whom I asked about whether I needed to learn Mishnah *Yoma*. And when he finished telling the story he smiled and asked me if I understood the connection between the Maharsham's decision and my case involving Reb Yaakobovitch's wagon.

"I nodded and said, 'Yes, the rav means to say that it is possible that the wagon was returned intact to Reb Yaakobovitch's house only because it was known and manifest to Hashem that a few minutes later I would promise to learn Mishnah *Yoma* by heart.'

"'Indeed,' said the rav. 'Of course I cannot say what would have happened if you hadn't taken anything upon yourself. But I can say that it is at least possible that because of your decision to learn, the wagon was returned to its place. Therefore, you cannot release yourself from learning what you took upon yourself.'"

Here Rebbe Mendel finished his story and said with a smile, "I cannot determine with certainty why Hashem rewarded you with the hearing of three stories at one time, but it is certainly possible that you got this reward because it is known and manifest that from now until the end of the day you will pay attention and learn with gusto — despite the heat and despite the thoughts of lumber and bonfires."

Section 4

CAST YOUR BREAD...

# CHAPTER 14

# THE KIDDUSH CUP

O ne day, right before Sukkos, we were learning the book of *Koheles* — which many shuls read on Shabbos during the festival. When we came to the verse, "Cast your bread [as if] over the water, for with the passing of time you will retrieve [its reward],"[1] Rebbe Mendel explained it thus: "When a person helps someone else, he should know that the good deed he does may come back to benefit him in the future." It was hard for us to imagine how one small gesture could help us later on, so Rebbe Mendel said, "Let me tell you the tale of the silver Kiddush cup. That might help you understand." And this is the story he told us:

*The events at the beginning of this story took place about forty years ago. The end of the school year was approaching, and the pupils in the eighth grade wanted to buy their rebbe a worthy present.*

*After long discussion, it was decided to buy the rebbe a silver Kiddush cup and to have engraved on it a few words of thanks. After the money had been collected by two of the pupils, Avi and Yossi, their friends said*

---

1. *Koheles* 11:1.

to them, "'To someone who begins a mitzvah you say finish it'[2] — so go and buy a nice cup."

That very day, Avi and Yossi went to the silver goods store called "Silver." When they entered, they were overwhelmed with the tremendous variety of Kiddush cups, and many other lovely silver objects. They didn't have to wait long before the owner of the store, Mr. Goldman, approached them, saying, "May I help you, boys?"

"Yes," answered Avi. "We want to buy a silver Kiddush cup for our rebbe — you know, it's the end of the year, and we're finishing cheder."

"Are you looking for sterling silver or for something silver-plated?" asked Mr. Goldman.

"Sterling silver," said Avi and Yossi together.

"A worthy gift, but expensive!" stated Mr. Goldman. "Forgive me for asking, but do you have enough money? I must tell you — a sterling silver Kiddush cup costs at least one hundred and fifty liras. So before you begin to look…" (Note: The lira was the unit of currency at that time.)

"That's all right," Yossi answered quickly and patted his pocket. There, in a handkerchief, were the coins and bills that they had collected from the pupils of the class.

"Fine," answered Mr. Goldman, and he went over to one of the glass-fronted cabinets that lined the walls of the store. "Do you want one with a stem or without?"

The two youngsters hesitated. Mr. Goldman took out ten Kiddush cups, put them on the counter and said, "Look at these, and decide which one you are interested in; just be careful! In the meantime, I am going wait on other customers." He left Avi and Yossi deliberating, and turned to an older couple who had just come into the store.

After much difficulty, Avi and Yossi reached an agreement and

---

2. Mishnah *Rosh Hashanah* 1:8.

chose a cup that didn't look especially expensive, but nevertheless was distinguished. They approached Mr. Goldman and informed him of their decision. Mr. Goldman regarded the cup and said, "You have good taste! Do you want to have a few words engraved on it?"

"Of course," Avi hastened to answer, and he took a slip of paper out of his pocket on which was written the text that had been agreed upon by the members of the class. "How much will the engraving cost us?"

"Only ten liras," said Mr. Goldman. "Accordingly, the price of the cup is one hundred and eighty liras, and together with the engraving the price is one hundred and ninety. Are you also interested in a saucer for the cup?"

"We were interested," said Yossi, "but it seems to me that we don't have enough money even for the cup itself. We have only one hundred and seventy liras. Can you give us a discount?"

"I am willing to sell you the Kiddush cup for one hundred and seventy liras instead of one hundred and eighty, but you will have to forgo the engraving," said Mr. Goldman patiently.

"Without the engraving the whole present is pointless," stated Avi.

"In which case, choose one of these," said Mr. Goldman, pointing to four of the Kiddush cups. "Each one costs only one hundred and fifty liras, so even after the engraving you will have ten liras left over. Or go over to that small cupboard, in which you will find splendid cups that are not sterling silver but silver-plated."

Once again Avi and Yossi conferred and reached the decision that they really wanted to buy the cup that they first chose (whose price, as was mentioned, after the discount and including the engraving was one hundred and eighty liras). The two friends didn't know what to do, when suddenly an idea flashed into Avi's brain.

"Mr. Goldman," he said, "we are choosing the first cup, and want to engrave on it a few words, but because we're ten liras short, we wanted to offer to do some work for you. School will be out soon, and we will be happy to give you a few hours of our time. We simply must take this cup, and we cannot forgo the engraving."

Mr. Goldman looked at Avi and at Yossi and said, "I would like to help you very much, but what can you do for me? Wait! I have an idea. You see the big display window there? It hasn't been washed in a long time. If you take it upon yourselves to wash it in the next few days, I will give you the cup, with the engraving, for just one hundred and seventy liras. Do you agree?"

Avi immediately answered, "Yes!" Yossi wanted to agree, but he knew that he was going to be traveling with his family for the next two weeks, so he couldn't.

"That being the case," said Mr. Goldman warmly, "let's do it like adults." He took a piece of paper out of a drawer and wrote:

> *I hereby promise to wash the display window in the silver goods store called "Silver" before the twentieth of Av 5725.*

"Sign your name here, please," said Mr. Goldman, pointing to the paper.

Avi took the pen and quickly signed, "Avraham Yeshayahu Ze'ev Raphael Menashe."

Mr. Goldman stared at the long name and said. "Five names? Besides, you didn't write your last name."

Avi smiled and said, "Just four names; Menashe is the family name. At first, I had just three names: Avraham Yeshayahu after the Chazon Ish, and Ze'ev after a relative. The name Raphael was added when I was sick as a child."

"May you always be healthy," said Mr. Goldman. He took the paper and quickly put it into the bottom of his cash register. Then he said to the two friends, "Come back tomorrow afternoon. The cup will be ready by then, God-willing. Good-bye."

"Thank you!" cried Avi and Yossi, and the boys went on their way.

So, the school year came to an end. The cup was given with much ceremony to the rebbe, Rav Lipkin. Summer vacation began, and the matter of Goldman's display window was entirely forgotten — by both the boys and Mr. Goldman.

\*　　　\*　　　\*

Twenty-five years passed since Avi and Yossi bought the cup for their eighth-grade rebbe. Avi was now none other than Rav Avraham Menashe, a respected and prominent man.

It came to pass that one of Rav Avraham's relatives honored him as sandek at his son's bris. As a sign of gratitude and esteem, Rav Avraham decided to buy a silver Kiddush cup for the infant. In order to do that, he went to the fondly remembered silver goods store called Silver.

The elder Goldman had given up the management of the business long before and transferred the ownership of the store to his son, but the store itself had not changed at all.

Upon entering the store, Rav Avraham approached Mr. Goldman and said, "Shalom! I would like to buy a silver Kiddush cup without a stem, with a matching saucer."

The younger Goldman pointed to a row of cups and said, "Please look at these."

Rav Avraham did not tarry long. He picked up one of the cups and said, "I am interested in this one. Do you have a matching saucer?"

"Of course," answered Mr. Goldman (the younger), and specified the price of the two items together.

"I would be interested in having a few words engraved on the cup," said Rav Avraham.

*"Of course," said Mr. Goldman, placing a piece of paper and a pen before Rav Avraham. "Here, write the words that you want to have engraved on this."*

*Rav Avraham took the pen and quickly wrote:*

> *On the occasion of your entry into the covenant of Avraham Avinu, a"h.*
>
> *From your cousin and sandek,*
> *Avraham Yeshayahu Ze'ev Raphael Menashe*

*Goldman the younger picked up the paper and said, "Fine. Come... Just a minute! Is this your name, sir?"*

*"Yes," answered Rav Avraham, smiling. "You undoubtedly wonder about such a long name, but Menashe is the family name, and Raphael was added when I was sick, and..."*

*"May you always be healthy," said Mr. Goldman. "You don't have to render an account to me. But for some reason, your name reminds me of something. One moment — what was it? Nu...! Avraham Yeshayahu... Menashe... That's it! I remember now. In the depths of the cash register there is a strange note... Wait, see for yourself."*

*Mr. Goldman burrowed in the depths of the cash register and took out from its midst a slip of paper that was already yellowed, and on which was written:*

> *I hereby promise to wash the display window in the silver goods store called "Silver" before the twentieth of Av 5725.*
>
> *Avraham Yeshayahu Ze'ev Raphael Menashe*

Rav Avraham jumped as if he had been bitten by a snake. "Oy vey! How could I have forgotten this? It is clear that I promised to do it. We were left owing ten liras, and in exchange I promised to wash the display window. And now I owe ten liras, but what should I do? In the meantime, the currency changed from liras to shekels. If I pay ten shekels — there will be a problem of interest here, and if I pay ten liras — they aren't worth a thing."

"Null and void!" cried Goldman the younger. "You are completely for-given."

"Thank you," said Rav Avraham, "but you cannot forgive me, because my promise was made to your father, may he live and be well, and even if you can forgive me, I do not wish to accept it. Therefore, the only possibil-ity is for me to wash the display window."

"Absolutely not! A distinguished rav such as you should wash the display window?" exclaimed Goldman. "Have I not told you that you are completely forgiven?"

"Yes, and I thank you. But I still want to keep my word. I will wash the display window," said Rav Avraham. "I will fulfill the promise I made and the words I spoke."

"A very nice sentiment," said Mr. Goldman, "but in my opinion, it will be a disgrace for you to stand in the street and wash the display win-dow."

"All right," concurred Rav Avraham, "so I will wash it at night."

And neither Rav Avraham nor Goldman the younger knew that by the end of the evening, the latter would owe a debt of gratitude to Rav Avraham and would consider him "paid in full."

Late that night, Rav Avraham left his house with a couple of rags and a bottle of cleaner feeling great joy. "With the help of Hashem Yisbarach, I am about to repay my debt," he thought to himself.

As he was approaching the store, he suddenly heard a strange noise coming from the roof. Rav Avraham stopped. For a moment there was *quiet, but then the sound started again. Rav Avraham approached the store stealthily. He then heard a scraping sound.*

*Rav Avraham peeked carefully through the store window and almost cried out. A rope ladder was being lowered from the ceiling into the store, and a pair of legs began to descend.*

*"Thief!" Rav Avraham said to himself in alarm. "A robbery is being carried out here before my eyes. I must call the police."*

*In the meantime, Rav Avraham hid himself as he watched the thief climb down the ladder into the store.*

*"A bad business," said Rav Avraham. "By the time I call the police, this guy will empty out the cash register and the display shelves and get away on the rope ladder. He can do that in a minute, whereas it will take me two minutes just to get to the nearest telephone."*

*He thought for a moment, and with Hashem's help an idea flashed into his brain. "I will climb up onto the roof of the store and pull the rope ladder up. That way the thief will remain in the store and will not be able to leave, and then I will rush to call the police."*

*The thief had conveniently left a wooden ladder standing against the wall behind the store. Rav Avraham quickly climbed up to the roof and immediately located the hatch. The locked hatch had obviously been forced open, and that must have been the noise Rav Avraham had originally heard. He grabbed the rope ladder, which was tied to the open hatch; but it was too late. As he began to pull it up, the thief noticed, rushed to the disappearing ladder, and grabbed the end.*

*Rav Avraham pulled with all his strength, but the burglar's hands were stronger, and the ladder started being pulled very slowly downward.*

*Rav Avraham's face became red, and his knuckles became white. And then the ladder's lowest rung suddenly broke, and the burglar fell hard to the floor.*

*Rav Avraham quickly pulled up the rope ladder, gasping from the*

*Rav Avraham grabbed the rope ladder and so did the thief.*

great effort he had just expended. He began to make his way to the ladder standing against the back wall of the building, in order to climb down and call the police.

The burglar, meanwhile, got shakily to his feet and called out, "Wait a minute, mister…" He sounded as if he were pleading.

Rav Avraham didn't respond. He wanted to leave the place quickly, but then the burglar said again, "Mister, please stop! I beg you to wait a minute."

Rav Avraham stopped and listened to the burglar's words.

"My parents are old," he said. "They haven't had any nachas from me. Who knows what will happen to them when they learn about this… Please, let me go!"

"And who knows what will become of you… what crimes you will yet commit?" answered Rav Avraham from the roof.

"And what good will it do if I sit in jail?" the burglar asked. "You know that prison is where little criminals just become bigger criminals. Let me go. You won't be sorry if you do."

Rav Avraham hesitated for a moment, and then the burglar spoke again. "Quickly, mister. Lower the rope before a patrol car passes. I will yet return to the right path. See, I am not taking a thing from the store. Let me go. I will yet return to the right path …"

Rav Avraham sighed, picked up the rope ladder and threw it into the store.

A moment later the two stood together on the roof. The young man shook Rav Avraham's hand and said, "Mister, you won't regret this, I assure you."

"I hope not," said Rav Avraham. "What is your name?"

"Pinchas. Pinchas Kagan," said the young man.

Both men descended the wooden ladder. As they parted, Rav Avraham said, "Good luck, Pinchas. May Hashem accompany you all the days of your life."

*A moment later, the young man had disappeared into the darkness.*

*Rav Avraham hurried to the nearest public telephone and called Mr. Goldman. He came to the store immediately. When he found that everything was in its place and nothing was missing, he hugged Rav Avraham and said, "Baruch Hashem for having caused you to forget about washing the display window until this very day. Because of that, I was saved from a great loss. Now, certainly, you no longer have to clean the window."*

*"Fine," Rav Avraham agreed. "But do me a favor and tell your father that I came and paid what I owed. I wish to be clean of any obligation 'to God and to Yisrael.'"[3]*

*"I will tell him and let you know when I have," said Mr. Goldman.*

*Rav Avraham thanked him and hurried off to daven vasikin, since the day was already breaking.*

∗       ∗       ∗

*Fifteen years passed since Rav Avraham climbed the roof of the silver store and let the thief go. Rav Avraham was now fifty-four years old and had ten grandchildren. He had great nachas from all his children and grandchildren — except for his ben zekunim, "the son of his old age," Binyamin.*

*Even when he was very young, Binyamin did not reveal a great desire to learn, but the matter worsened when he began to learn Gemara. Binyamin didn't understand and didn't want to understand. His father tried to review the lessons with him, and would have been happy to explain the material over and over again, just so his son would understand. But Binyamin didn't have the patience to sit for a long time.*

*Binyamin's sister's son, Menachem, was only a year younger than Binyamin. Menachem was a diligent boy and did well in cheder, and the*

---

3. *Bemidbar* 32:22.

relatives always whispered, "See, the nephew is such a good student, whereas the uncle… Nu, what can you say? Exactly the opposite."

What they all whispered softly, Binyamin felt, and utter despair seized him. His learning was loathsome to him. Even the small effort that he had put into his studies before then was completely withdrawn. His presence in the classroom became a nuisance, and the principal, Rav Geller, was compelled to ask Rav Avraham to meet with him.

"I get great nachas from your grandchildren, Rav Avraham," said Rav Geller, "but unfortunately, I cannot say the same about your youngest son. If we don't do something immediately, he will go from bad to worse, God forbid. And besides that, I don't know if we can keep him in the cheder."

"I understand," sighed Rav Avraham. "My youngest child, my ben zekunim — apparently I did not succeed in raising him properly."

"Don't blame yourself, Rav Avraham. I have an idea. What do you think of having Binyamin learn in the cheder in the morning and having him tutored by an avreich in the afternoon?"

"But what avreich can handle him? After all, he doesn't want to learn!" cried Rav Avraham in despair. "That would just take him out of the cheder without bringing any benefit."

"Listen," said Rav Geller, "you have nothing to lose. Try my idea for one month. I recently got a recommendation about a special avreich who knows how to reach difficult children, and who also has an excellent ability to explain…"

There was a small silence. "Okay," Rav Avraham sighed again, "I agree. What must I do?"

"Just call him," said the principal. "Here is his telephone number. His name is Pinchas Kagan, and he learns in kollel Ohel haTorah."

"Fine," said Rav Avraham. "It's strange, but I'm sure I've heard that name before."

"It's no wonder you've heard of him. He is a well-known avreich," said Rav Geller.

We, the children of the class, had been listening attentively. We also recognized the name Pinchas Kagan. Rebbe Mendel paid no attention to our cries of excitement and recognition and continued his story.

*What can I say? The unbelievable happened. Reb Pinchas knew exactly how to open Binyamin's heart. He discovered how talented Binyamin was and how successful he could be. He explained the Gemara to him well, and most important — he made him love learning. Binyamin changed into a different boy. Rav Avraham was beside himself with happiness. He called Reb Pinchas every week to thank him.*

*Chanukah was approaching, and Rav Avraham, who felt immensely grateful to Reb Pinchas, decided to buy him a gift. After some deliberation, he went to the silver goods store called Silver under the management of Mr. Goldman (the younger, who was already not so young anymore). He bought an ornate Chanukah menorah and had engraved on it: "To Reb Pinchas Kagan, from the Menashe family," and went to the home of the dear avreich.*

*After many refusals and repeated entreaties, Reb Pinchas agreed to accept the menorah.*

*Rav Avraham said to him, "I have no words. You really saved my son. In my mind's eye I already saw him going downhill, God forbid. And now, what a flower you succeeded in growing for me!"*

*"Yes, things like that happen, baruch Hashem," said Reb Pinchas. "People can sometimes be on the threshold of actual criminality, and they turn into different people in a minute. You must have heard that I am a ba'al teshuvah."*

*"I didn't know that. But what of it?" asked Rav Avraham, feeling a bit uncomfortable.*

*"I mean that if you want to thank someone in this world for your son's progress, it isn't me," said Reb Pinchas.*

"Who is it? And how is he connected to my son?" asked Rav Avraham.

"I myself do not know who he is," sighed Reb Pinchas. He fell silent for a moment and then said, "I see that you bought this menorah at Silver."

"Indeed," answered Rav Avraham and, astonished, added, "but why is that important?"

"It's not important," answered Reb Pinchas, "but it is connected to the matter we were talking about. I don't know why I am telling you this, but at the moment before I dropped into the abyss — the moment before I sank completely — a precious man saved me when we were on the roof of the silver goods store…"

"Pinchas Kagan! I don't believe it!" exclaimed Rav Avraham. "Are you the one for whom I lowered the rope ladder?"

Reb Pinchas leaped from his place. "I don't believe it!" he said. "Are you the one who responded to my entreaties? Yes! You are the one! And so, whom should you thank for your son Binyamin's progress? You should thank yourself! And of course Hashem, Who put pity for me into your heart. And now tell me, have I disappointed you?" And when he said this, Reb Pinchas opened wide his arms and embraced Rav Avraham.

"You saved me from the cruel pit of prison. Did I not tell you that you would not be sorry for it?"

Rav Avraham was deeply moved. "Now I really feel the verse, 'Cast your bread over the water.' Everything I did, I really — and unknowingly — did for myself."

# CHAPTER 15

# MAGGID SHIUR

"**R**inah u'Tefillah" was a small shul with a small congregation. The only people who prayed there regularly during the week were seven elderly men, so before almost every *tefillah*, Noach the *gabbai* had to go out and find three more. And if it happened that one of the seven regulars didn't come, it was sometimes hard to make a minyan.

But Noach was not the kind of person who is discouraged by such problems, so the minyan continued to exist, and the routine was not broken.

Once, at a wedding, Noach ran into his old friend Yair. After they had greeted each other, Yair asked, "So, Noach, are you still pulling the old wagon?"

"What wagon are you talking about? I don't even have a car to pull a trailer with," answered Noach with a smile.

Yair laughed and said, "Don't pretend you don't understand. I was asking whether you are still the *gabbai* of that shul... what's it called?"

"Rinah u'Tefillah," answered Noach. "What kind of a question is that, am I still the *gabbai*? Of course I am. The shul is still in existence, and with Hashem's help will remain in existence and become stronger."

"So who is your *maggid shiur*?" asked Yair.

"*Maggid shiur*?" asked Noach. "We don't have any *shiurim* in the shul."

"Not even between *Minchah* and *Ma'ariv*?" asked Yair in surprise.

"It's not possible," said Noach. "There are just seven of us who daven there regularly, and we barely manage to get three more. We have to daven *Ma'ariv* as early as possible, so the passersby I drag in to make the *Minchah* minyan won't leave before *Ma'ariv*. Therefore, there is no time for a *shiur*."

"No time for a *shiur*?" exclaimed Yair. "Look around and you'll see how *shiurim* have multiplied, *baruch Hashem*! This phenomenom is truly a shining light in our generation. No *shiurim*? How can that be? A shul without *shiurim* is like *Minchah* without *Ashrei*."

Noach didn't answer. After a moment Yair added, "And besides, who said that the *shiur* has to be between *Minchah* and *Ma'ariv*?"

The two chatted about one thing and another until the band began playing its deafening music and the two got up to dance.

When Noach got home after the wedding he began to think about what Yair had said, and decided that, *b'ezras Hashem*, Congregation Rinah u'Tefillah would also have a daily Torah lesson.

Noach discussed the matter with the other six regulars, and the seven agreed to have a *shiur* for half an hour after *Ma'ariv* every weekday. They also agreed that the *shiur* should be on a relatively "easy" subject, since hardly any progress would be made in only half an hour with Gemara or another difficult subject.

Noach looked for a *maggid shiur*, and he found one — a young *avreich* named Reb Azriel. Reb Azriel agreed to give a *shiur*, and proposed that it be on the *Ein Yaakov*, a collection of Aggados and *divrei mussar* from the Gemara.

And so Reb Azriel came to the little shul every day to give a lesson to the seven regulars. He did it faithfully and asked for no payment.

It often happened that the eyelids of some of the listeners drooped during the *shiur*, and many times they began to argue about irrelevant things in the middle of the learning. Reb Azriel would become discouraged when this happened, and a thought would steal into his heart: "What are you doing here? There is no real Torah-learning to speak of, and you are not getting paid. This whole business is a waste of time that will bring no benefit to anyone in either this world or the next."

Reb Azriel pushed aside such thoughts until the day he broke.

It was when they were learning, in *maseches Chagigah,* about the length and width of the world and of the whole universe. The things that were written in the *Ein Yaakov* were deep and not understandable according to their plain meaning. Moreover, Reb Azriel himself had devoted a lot of time to preparing thoroughly for the *shiur* by studying the Maharsha on the Gemara as well as the *Eitz Yosef* and the *Anfei Yosef,* two commentaries in the *Ein Yaakov*.

But when the lesson began and Reb Azriel wanted to tell his listeners about the Maharsha's wonderful idea concerning the intention of the Gemara regarding the words "length,"

*Many times they would argue about irrelevant things.*

"width," "empty space," and other such concepts, an argument started. It sounded more or less like this:

"The length is the diameter of the Earth…"

"What are you talking about, the diameter? The diameter of the Earth is just eight thousand miles. No, no! Length means the circumference."

"That's also too small," said a third. "The Gemara means the distance from the Earth to the Sun."

"What are you talking about? That's a distance of ninety million miles."

"So maybe you think that it is referring to the distance between the Earth and the Moon?"

"Listen, I learned astronomy from Dr. Heller in Warsaw. So with all due respect…"

Reb Azriel tried to put an end to the senseless babble, but without success. Noach the *gabbai* said loudly, "Gentlemen, please! This is impossible. We came to learn, no?"

After this scolding, silence reigned for two minutes, and immediately with the next clause an argument about the size of the moon began, and so it happened that in the end Reb Azriel, Noach, and the six "sages" managed to learn just four and a half lines.

That very evening, Reb Azriel decided not to continue giving the *shiur*. Nevertheless, he went to consult with one of the *gedolei ha-dor*, to whom he was very close.

He poured his heart out before the rav and said, "There is no *mezakei ha-rabbim*, 'bringing merit to the many,' here. There is *bittul Torah* for me here. And maybe there is even *bittul Torah* for the men of the shul, because it would be better for them not to learn than to sit with the *Ein Yaakov* open and chatter."

The rav asked him, "They talk every day? They waste time during the entire *shiur*? Are there a few minutes of learning? Is there one person who does pay attention to the *shiur*?"

Reb Azriel answered hesitantly that indeed there were days when the men unquestionably learned, and even on days when they were extra loquacious there were two or three who were interested in learning and not talking.

The rav said to him, "It is worth it for even one person. It is worth it for even two minutes. Moreover, we have learned, 'He who goes but doesn't do earns the reward for going.'"[1]

"So the rav is instructing me to continue?" asked Reb Azriel.

"Continue and succeed!" exclaimed the rav, and added the last sentence of the *haftarah* for *parashas Ki Savo*: "The smallest will become a thousand and the youngest a great nation."[2]

And so Reb Azriel continued to give the *shiur*.

One day Rav Kirschenbaum, rosh yeshiva of Milchemtah shel Torah and a great and famous rabbi, came into Rinah u'Tefillah to daven *Ma'ariv*. The reason for his coming to the shul was not a happy one. His young daughter had been hospitalized early that morning with a serious illness. The family members — parents, older brothers and sisters, even cousins — quickly arranged to take turns staying with the little girl, so that, day or night, there would always be a family member by her bedside.

Rav Kirschenbaums's turn was from eight o'clock to eleven

---

1. *Pirkei Avos* 5:14.
2. *Yeshayahu* 60:22.

o'clock in the evening, at which time another family member would take his place. Because Rinah u'Tefillah was very close to the hospital, the rosh yeshiva stopped in to daven *Ma'ariv* there on his way from the yeshiva to the hospital. He prayed for a long time, and by the time he had finished Reb Azriel had already begun his *shiur.*

Rav Kirschenbaum did not want to leave the shul while the *shiur* was going on, because to do so might hurt the feelings of the young *avreich* who was giving the lesson. What did he do? In his great modesty, he sat down at the end of the table, picked up a copy of *Ein Yaakov,* opened it to the page that was being studied, and listened.

When Reb Azriel became aware of the rosh yeshiva, he quickly came to his feet in respect, but with a gesture the rosh yeshiva indicated that he should continue the *shiur.*

At first Reb Azriel was so flustered by finding himself giving a class in the presence of such a great rav that he could only stammer. But after a few seconds he recovered his composure and continued as usual. He came to a passage in the text that was very difficult to understand and explained it the way the Maharsha does.

The rosh yeshiva listened intently, and when Reb Azriel had finished said, "Interesting! I always understood the Maharsha's words differently, but the explanation you gave just now makes a lot of sense, and actually fits the text better."

Rav Kirschenbaum sat until the end of the *shiur,* and then immediately got up in order to get to the hospital. But before he left he took Reb Azriel aside and said, "*Yashar koach*! I enjoyed the *shiur* very much." Reb Azriel blushed, and mumbled an embarrassed thanks.

The same thing happened the next day. Rav Kirschenbaum stopped at Rinah u'Tefillah to daven *Ma'ariv* on his way to the hospital, and as soon as he had finished davening, he sat down and participated in the *shiur* like everyone else.

As it happened, Rav Kirschenbaum's daughter had to stay in the hospital for several weeks, and so every weekday the rosh yeshiva came to pray *Ma'ariv* at the shul, and he always remained to hear the lesson in *Ein Yaakov*.

Back on the second day that the rosh yeshiva attended the *shiur,* Reb Azriel approached him and said that it would be appropriate for the rosh yeshiva to give the *shiur,* but Rav Kirschenbaum said to Reb Azriel with a smile, "If I give the *shiur,* I won't have the pleasure of hearing your explanations, and therefore I am willing to forgo the honor."

One day, a young man who learned in Milchemtah shel Torah happened to pass the shul at *Ma'ariv* time and noticed that Rav Kirschenbaum went in. For some time, the *bachur* had been looking for an opportunity to speak to his rosh yeshiva, so he, too, turned in to daven *Ma'ariv*. When he finished, he sat down to wait for Rav Kirschenbaum to finish his prayers, and when the rosh yeshiva had finished the *bachur* got up and walked toward him. However, Rav Kirschenbaum pointed to his watch as a sign that he would talk to him later, and stepped quickly to the table around which sat Reb Azriel and the seven oldsters. The rosh yeshiva picked up an *Ein Yaakov* and the *bachur* who wanted to talk to him also sat down. Noach the *gabbai* hastened to bring him, too, a volume of *Ein Yaakov*.

At first the *bachur* thought that it was only so as not to embarrass Reb Azriel that the rosh yeshiva picked up the book. He was sure that Rav Kirschenbaum was thinking, not about *Ein Yaakov,* but about the *sugya* that was currently being studied in the yeshiva. Or perhaps the rav was thinking about his sick daughter. But to his great surprise, the young man saw that the rosh yeshiva was paying attention to every word spoken by the unknown *maggid shiur.* This time, the subject of the lesson was Korach and his followers (Perek Cheilek in *maseches Sanhedrin*). Everything was perfectly clear, but the rosh yeshiva asked questions as if he were a *talmid* sitting before his rebbe, and Reb Azriel answered him clearly, displaying a complete understanding of the text.

That day was the first time in the history of the *shiur* that Reb Noach was able to say *Kaddish d'Rabbanan* after it. (*Kaddish d'Rabbanan* is the Kaddish that is said after learning, and it includes a special blessing for rabbis and their students and all those who occupy themselves with Torah.) As you know, Kaddish is said only in a minyan, and every day there were only eight people in the shul at the end of the *shiur:* the seven regulars and Reb Azriel. When Rav Kirschenbaum joined the *shiur,* they still didn't have a minyan, but that day there were finally ten: the seven regulars, Reb Azriel, the rosh yeshiva and the *bachur.*

The next day, sensational news swept through the yeshiva: Rav Kirschenbaum, the rosh yeshiva, who, as is well-known, sits at his daughter's bedside in the hospital every evening, first goes to hear a *shiur* on *Ein Yaakov* given by an unknown *avreich* in a dilapidated little shul. Everyone thought that the rosh yeshiva went to the little shul especially to hear the *shiur,* and they concluded that it must be a spectacular *shiur* indeed.

And so, the following evening ten students from the yeshiva came to Rinah u'Tefillah to listen to the *shiur.* Each day, more *bachurim* came, and, in the end, about thirty-five people were attending the *shiur* regularly. Twelve men with books crowded around the shaky table, and the rest stood and just listened. Needles to say, in the course of the *shiur* the *bachurim* asked challenging questions, all of which Reb Azriel answered with skill and knowledge. Sometimes the questions and answers went on and on, however, until Noach the *gabbai* said, "Enough! That's enough arguing. We are ordinary Jews and we just want to understand the *peshat*." Then the *bachurim* would be quiet for a while and Reb Azriel would continue explaining the words of *Chazal* in his clear and pleasing way.

The daily streaming of so many young men to the little shul did not escape the attention of the people who lived nearby. A few of the more curious went to see what it was all about. They told their neighbors about the *shiur*, and some of them went to hear it for themselves, and then told *their* neighbors, and so on, so that very quickly the word got around the neighborhood that it would be a shame to miss the daily *shiur* of the very learned Reb Azriel. Thus, every day more people came to the shul for *Minchah*, *Ma'ariv*, and the *shiur*.

Reb Noach mused that there were never more than sixty men in the shul on Rosh Hashanah and Yom Kippur, so he could hardly believe his eyes when there were eighty or more davening *Minchah-Ma'ariv* on a weekday. And all this on account of the little *shiur* that he had established!

The new people in the shul donated scores of *Ein Yaakov* sets. And because there was such a crowd, Reb Azriel had to deliver his *shiur* from behind a *shtender* in the front of the shul, even though he would much rather have sat at the table.

During this time, the rosh yeshiva, Rav Kirschenbaum,

didn't miss the *shiur* even once. Then, after the *shiur* one evening, he came over to Reb Azriel and said, "Reb Azriel, *baruch Hashem* my daughter has recovered. She will be released from the hospital tomorrow, God willing. I will no longer be coming here for *Ma'ariv*, and I am afraid I will not be able to attend your wonderful *shiur* anymore. I don't have to tell you how happy I am that my daughter is coming home, but at the same time I am sorry to be leaving your *shiur*." Reb Azriel blushed and thanked the rosh yeshiva for the compliment, saying he was much too kind.

The rosh yeshiva did indeed stop coming to the *shiur*, but, *baruch Hashem*, what happened because he came, remained. People continued to come to the shul in droves to hear Reb Azriel's *shiur* and to daven there as well.

Three years later, Congregation Rinah u'Tefillah would have been unrecognizable to someone who hadn't seen it change. The building had been renovated and enlarged, new furniture purchased, and a sound system installed. The *shiur* in *Ein Yaakov* after *Ma'ariv* continued, but there was also a *daf yomi* class an hour before *Minchah*. Reb Azriel delivered both *shiurim* in his usual erudite way to scores of people who overflowed the renovated shul.

Then Reb Azriel understood the words of his rabbi, who had said, "The smallest will become a thousand and the youngest a great nation."

One day, Reb Noach ran into his old friend Yair, whom Reb Noach had encountered at a wedding some years before.

"Well! *Shalom aleichem*, Yair!" exclaimed Noach.

"*Aleichem shalom*, Noach!" cried Yair. "*Nu*? Are you still pulling the wagon?"

"Oho!" said Noach, and smiled. Then he seized Yair's hands and held them tightly in his own for a moment.

"What is it?" asked Reb Yair.

"I will tell you," said Noach. "Do you remember, Yair, the story about how Rav Chanina ben Dosa once found some hens and cared for them and their offspring until he had a flock of chickens, whereupon he sold them and bought a nanny goat and a billy goat, and how after a number of years, when the owner of the chickens came and asked for what he had lost, Rav Chanina ben Dosa showed him a flock of goats and said, 'Lo, yours is before you'?"

"Of course I remember that story," said Yair. "But what is the connection between Rav Chanina ben Dosa and your shul?"

"Very simple," answered Noach. "You asked if I am still pulling the wagon. Accordingly I would like to tell you that the wagon has turned into a bus, and it is not I who pulls it. Thanks to God, we have a good driver."

"The wagon has turned into a bus? I don't understand," said Yair. "All I wanted was to ask how your little minyan is getting along."

"You will understand soon," said Noach. "In another twenty minutes we will be davening *Minchah* at Rinah u'Tefillah. Will you come and daven with me?"

"Yes, of course. I haven't davened *Minchah* yet and I will be happy to complete a minyan," answered Yair.

As they approached the shul, Reb Noach gestured toward the large, handsome building and said with feeling, "This is the bus I was talking about. The little shul — a wagon, as you put it — has in the course of time become a large bus, just as some hens once turned into a flock of goats. But in truth, this beautiful bus belongs to you. It is what it is because of you — because of the advice you gave me to establish a *shiur* in the shul."

The two men entered the shul in time to see fifty men listening intently to the end of the *daf yomi* lesson. Yair was so moved that he couldn't speak. He davened *Minchah* and *Ma'ariv*, and stayed for the *shiur* in *Ein Yaakov*. Afterwards, he took Noach aside and, pointing to Reb Azriel, said, "It seems to me that a large shul like this one needs a rav. And it also seems to me that you've already got yourselves the perfect candidate!"

# CHAPTER 16

# *TEFILLAH B'TZIBBUR*

When we were learning in class about the laws and importance of *tefillah b'tzibbur*, praying with a minyan, Rebbe Mendel said, "Let me tell you about Reb Yerachmiel and how strict he was about praying with a minyan."

*This happened twenty years ago. I had to travel from Bnei Brak to Haifa. There was then no express bus number 970 (which is remembered favorably in another story). Therefore I took a bus number 921. I don't know if that line still exists, but anybody who ever rode it will remember that the trip from Bnei Brak to Haifa was very tiring. The buses on that line stopped at every bus stop and at every settlement, no matter how small or isolated, in order to gather together all the "scattered of Israel" and take them to their desired destinations. Consequently, the trip took a very long time. The man sitting next to me, a talmid chacham named Reb Yerachmiel, didn't want to waste the time doing nothing, so he began to "talk in learning" with me. So we sat and talked divrei Torah, and right after I explained the question of Rabbi Shimon Shkop on the laws of a Kohen with a defect, Reb Yerachmiel suddenly said, "Oy! I thought I would be able to daven Minchah in Haifa. But now I see that there is still a long way to go, and at this rate I won't make it before sundown."*

*I smiled and said, "If you are wondering whether to daven standing or* sitting, I will tell you that when riding it is preferable to pray while sitting, because that way one can concentrate more."

"I, too, have heard that," said Reb Yerachmiel, "but there is no minyan here, and my practice is to daven with a minyan."

"What can you do?" I asked. "You have no choice but to pray alone."

"What do you mean, my friend, what can I do? I am fifty years old and it has never happened that I didn't pray with a minyan except when I was sick, and you ask, What can you do? The bus will soon reach Moshav Te'enah, where it seems to me that observant Jews also live. I will get off there. I'm sure I will be able to reach the shul there in time for Minchah."

"Are you obligated to do that?" I asked.

"I don't know if I am obligated or not obligated, but that is what I am going to do, my friend," said Reb Yerachmiel. "When is the most favorable time to pray? When the congregation is praying!"[1] As the bus approached the settlement, Reb Yerachmiel rang the bell and made his way down the aisle to the front door.

As the bus came to a stop, the driver, who appeared to be non-religious and of Sephardic origin, turned toward Reb Yerachmiel and asked, "Why are you getting off here? You bought a ticket for Haifa."

"I did indeed want to go to Haifa," answered Reb Yerachmiel, "but now I want to get off here."

"You know I can't return the extra money," said the driver apologetically as he opened the door.

"I know," said Reb Yerachmiel to the driver, "but that's all right." And, as he got off the bus and began to walk quickly toward the settlement, he added, "Yashar koach!"

The driver turned to me and asked, "What's with him? He wants to

---

1. See *Berachos* 8a.

go to Haifa, and all of a sudden decides to get off in the middle of no-where."

I briefly explained to the driver why Reb Yerachmiel had gotten off the bus.

"You're kidding!" said the driver in astonishment. "He got off just so he could pray with a minyan? Listen, that's a real Jew! That's a tzaddik! He doesn't do things halfway! He goes straight."

What can I say? I felt a little ashamed of myself. To hear such a "shmuze" from a non-religious person…

We continued on our way, but as we approached Pardes Hannah, the bus stopped unexpectedly because of a tremendous traffic jam.

"What's going on?" asked several passengers.

"How should I know?" answered the driver. "All I know is that there's a traffic jam."

After a few minutes during which nothing moved, the driver got off the bus to find out what was happening. It turned out that about three hundred yards ahead of us there had been a traffic accident, and we ended up waiting a long time.

The driver grumbled, but suddenly said to me, "You see? Your friend, the tzaddik with the long beard, didn't lose a thing. He prayed and then caught the next bus, but he'll get to Haifa the same time we do."

In the end, after half an hour of waiting and another forty-five min-utes of weary travel, we got to Haifa, tired and impatient.

✳ ✳ ✳

"Late that evening I was waiting for the bus back to Bnei Brak, when whom do you think I saw approaching the bus stop?"

"Reb Yerachmiel!" shouted Meshulam and Moishie.

"That's right," answered Rebbe Mendel. "Reb Yerachmiel

himself! When he reached the bus stop I told him everything that had happened to us, and I asked him how and when he had gotten to Haifa…"

*Reb Yerachmiel answered, "Listen carefully and you will understand that one never loses by doing a mitzvah. Imagine this: Immediately after Minchah, I started back to the bus stop. I hadn't even reached it when a car stopped next to me. The driver was one of the men who had been at Minchah. He asked me where I was going. When I told him I was going to Haifa, he said that he was also going there, and invited me to go with him.*

*"Of course I accepted the invitation. The gentleman took a much faster route than the bus's, and was even so kind as to take me to the part of the city I was going to."*

*"Who would have believed it?" I cried. "That's a real marvel!"*

*The bus arrived then, and when we got on we saw that our driver for the way back was the same one who had taken us to the north.*

*He was happy to see Reb Yerachmiel and said, "I told your friend that you didn't lose a thing from performing a mitzvah. We were stuck in a traffic jam for a long time, so you must have gotten to Haifa at the same time we did."*

*The Reb Yerachmiel told the driver what he had told me.*

*The driver made cries of astonishment and said excitedly, "You really are a tzaddik! God made a miracle happen for you. I tell you, the man who took you was Eliyahu haNavi!"*

*"Nu, don't exaggerate," said Reb Yerachmiel, smiling. "Not Eliyahu haNavi. But it is certain that he was Heaven-sent."*

*The driver was silent for a moment and then said, "You know what? I would like you to bless me."*

*Reb Yerachmiel cleared his throat in embarrassment and after a moment said, "My blessing is that you should succeed in all you do. But only* in things for the good, you understand. Do good things. I bless you with not being able to do bad things."

"And bless me with good health and a good livelihood, too," asked the driver.

"I bless you that you should have good health and a good livelihood, but I am a simple Jew, so don't be surprised if my blessings don't come to pass."

"I'm sure they will come to pass," said the driver. "My mother told me that even the blessing of an ordinary person comes to pass."

"That's true," said Reb Yerachmiel. "The blessing of an ordinary person should not be taken lightly. And since that is so, I ask you to bless me."

The driver laughed and said, "I bless you with all the blessings in the world." With that the conversation ended, and Reb Yerachmiel sat down next to me.

⋆          ⋆          ⋆

Fifteen years passed since that episode. Then one day, about five years ago, I was walking down the street in Bnei Brak when I saw Reb Yerachmiel walking in my direction.

"Oho! Shalom aleichem," he said. "Do you know, I've been looking for you for fifteen years."

"Why?" I asked. "What happened?"

"The answer you gave me to Rav Shimon's question about the Kohen with a defect…"

"Oh, yes!" I said. "What about the answer?"

"Please forgive me," said Reb Yerachmiel, "but you didn't explain it the way that Rav Shimon explains it. If you look, you will see that…"

So we "talked in learning" for ten minutes, and when we finished, Reb Yerachmiel asked me what I do for a living.

"I am a teacher of young children," I answered, "and I also learn a little myself."

"Aha! A teacher of young children! If so, I have a story for you that you absolutely must tell your pupils."

"I am all ears," I said. Reb Yerachmiel began:

"I'm sure you remember that on that trip to Haifa, during which you discussed Rav Shimon Shkop's question with me, I got off the bus in the middle of the trip in order to daven Minchah with a minyan. The bus driver said that in the merit of my insistence on davening with a minyan, I got to Haifa very quickly. Well, the story doesn't end there. The rest of the story is enough to make your hair stand on end.

"Two years ago, I went on a fundraising trip on behalf of my yeshiva. I found myself in Miami Beach, Florida.

"I needed to visit a certain wealthy man who lived a considerable distance from my hotel. We had a successful meeting, and I received a substantial donation from him. As I was ready to leave, he gave me a warning.

"'At this time of day, when it is already dark, it's not a good idea to walk around in the city. If you take my advice, you will go straight to the nearest bus stop. And another bit of advice: Don't take taxis. There are all kinds of shady characters roaming around Miami. More than once someone has gotten into a car that looked like a taxicab and was then robbed of all his money and valuables by the driver, who was an impostor. Travel only by organized public transportation.'

"Of course I decided to take his advice, and I waited at a marked bus stop. But when a bus hadn't come for a long time, I stopped a cab despite the man's warning. Before I got in, I looked closely at the driver. He looked like a kind and decent young man.

"'To the center of town, the Jefferson Hotel, please.' The driver nodded and politely said, 'Yes, sir.'

"After several minutes of a relaxed ride in the direction of downtown, the driver unexpectedly turned off the main road and raced out of the city.

"'Where are you going?' I shouted. 'Stop immediately!'

"'Don't make trouble,' said the driver curtly. 'You're not in danger. We don't intend to harm you. We only want to take your money. But if you make trouble… what happens to you will be your own fault. And don't even think of trying to grab me or the steering wheel — we're going too fast. You'd better let me concentrate on driving.'

"I was paralyzed with fear, but I remembered that no harm ever comes to a person performing a mitzvah, whether he is on his way to do it or is returning from doing it.[2] And it was certainly true in my case, because I had not yet finished my fundraising trip. With these encouraging thoughts, I tried to strengthen myself."

Rebbe Mendel interrupted his telling of the story to say, "In my opinion, Reb Yerachmiel erred in this matter, because the Gemara that he mentioned says there that if the danger is likely — as it is with a shaky ladder — it is possible that the merit of the mitzvah will not protect the person, because it is forbidden to depend on a miracle. In the case of Reb Yerachmiel, it was a mistake not to heed the advice of the wealthy man."

Only after Rebbe Mendel was sure that we understood this comment did he continue to tell Reb Yerachmiel's spellbinding story.

"Finally, the car stopped with a screech of brakes — so suddenly that I nearly flew into the windshield. We were at a deserted spot in the middle of nowhere. The driver motioned for me to get out of the car.

"It was pitch dark, but I could make out a man coming toward us. 'I've brought you some new merchandise, Joe,' the driver cried as the strange man came up to me.

---

2. *Kiddushin* 39b.

*"I've brought you some new merchandise, Joe!"*

"The driver went through my pockets and took all my money and everything else of value. He said, 'We aren't going to be rough with you, and we won't do you any harm. We'll even show you the way back.' He pointed to a path several yards away and said, 'This path leads to the nearest town. As far as I know, cars never come this way, and it's a long way by foot. In the meantime, we'll disappear before you can get to the police.' Then the two men turned and started toward their car. I was left in the darkness with nothing.

"'Hey, you there!' I shouted at the top of my lungs.

"The men stopped and turned around.

"'Listen,' I said loudly, 'you just got three thousand dollars in cash, a bunch of checks, and a gold watch — about eight thousand dollars altogether. For that kind of a profit you can be nice guys and do me a small favor… take me back to town.'

"They burst out laughing.

"'Of course,' the one called Joe said. 'We'll take you back and you'll go straight to the police. Listen, why do you think we dragged you all the way out here? To take you back?'

"'I absolutely must be back in town no later than eleven o'clock tonight,' I said firmly.

"'What's the big rush?' asked Joe contemptuously.

"'Public prayer,' I answered. 'The Jewish religion requires men to pray three times a day — in the morning, in the afternoon, and at night — and the prayer has to be in a group of ten men, called a minyan.'

"The things I said made the driver double over with laughter. 'Now I've heard it all,' he said. 'An urgent request from a "customer" who says he has to get back to town as soon as possible — and he's not going to go to the police — ha ha!'

"'On my word; I promise!' I exclaimed firmly.

"'Tefillah b'tzibbur!' cried Joe. He came over to me quickly and peered intently at my face. "Aha! It is you!" he said. Turning to the other robber, he ordered, 'Return everything you took from him — immediately. I'm taking him back to town myself.' Then, turning back to me, he asked, 'Do you remember me?'

"I studied his face. I had a hazy memory of having seen him once or twice, but I couldn't place him. 'No,' I finally said. 'I believe I've seen you before, but I can't remember where or when' — all the time wondering why he was being so kind to me.

"'Righteous rabbi, I'm the bus driver who took you to Haifa and, later the same day, back to Bnei Brak, many years ago,' said Joe. 'I remember to this very day that you got off the bus in the middle of the trip in order to pray with a minyan. And it is only because you spoke of davening with a minyan now that I recognized you.'

"Joe told me to get into the car, and after he told the other man to wait for him, we set out on the drive back to town.

"'How is it that you got involved in crime?' I asked him.

"He was embarrassed and finally answered apologetically, 'It began with card-playing. I lost everything I had and ended up owing a tremendous amount of money. I had to steal to pay my debts. I stole and I played and I lost again, and I stole again until I was almost caught by the police and I had to escape to America. And as you see, I'm practicing the same profession here.' After a long pause, he continued, 'But every month I send money to my family in Israel, and almost all of the people I steal from are non-Jews, so maybe there's even some kind of a mitzvah in it...'

"I immediately started to admonish him, telling him that his 'mitzvah' would soon lead to a bad end for him, but that there was a way back. But he was adamant, and said that as far as he was concerned, there was no way back. Nothing I said had any influence. The discussion ended when we reached the center of the city. The last thing Joe said as I got out of the car was, 'Rabbi, maybe the time will come... who knows... maybe I will leave crime... maybe I will even be chozer b'teshuvah... If that actually happens, it will only be because of you and your tefillah b'tzibbur.'"

# CHAPTER 17
# *FIVE CORRECT ANSWERS*

Rebbe Mendel does not give grades less than eighty. When a pupil gets seventy-five on a test, for example, Rebbe Mendel writes, "Wrote seven and a half correct answers" on the test.

One time when we got our tests back, Shia, the boy who sits next to me, saw that the words, "Wrote seven correct answers" were written on his. He raised his hand and asked Rebbe Mendel, "The rebbe wrote on my test that I had seven correct answers, so what is my grade?" [You may be wondering why Shia didn't figure out for himself that seven correct answers means a grade of seventy. That's because the test consisted of twelve questions, so Shia didn't know whether seven correct answers meant seventy or less than that, because it was seven out of twelve, not seven out of ten. That's how Shia explained it to me.]

Rebbe Mendel looked at Shia and said, "You didn't get a grade. I just wanted you to know that you answered seven questions correctly."

"So that means it's a bad grade," declared Shia.

"I didn't say it's a bad grade," said Rebbe Mendel. "You wrote seven answers that are correct and complete."

"So why did the rebbe write 'ninety' on Nati's paper, and

not 'wrote nine correct answers'?" Shia asked again.

Rebbe Mendel sighed and said, "All right. I see that I am going to have to tell you about Hillel and Motti." So Rebbe Mendel told us this story:

*Until the middle of fifth grade, Hillel and Motti were considered pupils who were "average or below." That is, you couldn't say that they didn't try to pay attention, or that they didn't try to understand what was being taught, or that they didn't review it. But you could certainly say that they didn't ask questions, or answer questions, or get involved in classroom discussions. They simply didn't understand what was being taught. Once in a while one of them would raise his hand, but it was only to ask the rebbe to repeat his explanation — which the rebbe always did.*

*On written tests, they would usually get grades between fifty and sixty, but on oral tests they got nothing, because they were sure they didn't know the right answers to the questions and so didn't have enough confidence in themselves to try to answer them.*

*All this was, as I said, until the middle of fifth grade. Then, in the middle of the year, there was a change. Motti slowly began to change from being average or below to being average. By the beginning of sixth grade he was considered average or above, by the middle of the year he was a good pupil, and not long after he was considered a good and successful pupil.*

*In contrast, Hillel, Motti's best friend, remained in his previous status. He didn't understand what was being taught and didn't participate in the lessons. And so, while Motti's grades went from sixty to seventy and then from seventy to eighty and still higher, Hillel's remained what they had been at the beginning of the story — fifty or sixty.*

*Because Hillel and Motti were good friends, Motti didn't forget Hillel. He learned with him, reviewed the lessons with him, and tried to help him do better at his studies.*

One day when Hillel and Motti were learning b'chavrusa at school, they had a small argument. These were, more or less, the words they exchanged:

Hillel said, "I don't understand this. But please, don't waste your time trying to explain it to me. No matter what you do, I won't understand."

"You will understand it!" declared Motti. "Pay close attention. The Gemara says… "

"You're telling me to pay attention? Pay attention yourself!" burst out Hillel angrily. "I am not a good student, and that's all there is to it. I want to learn — you know I do — but my head just isn't so… and that's that. There's nothing you or anyone else can do."

"Stuff and nonsense!" answered Motti. "We've been friends since nursery school, and I know you're not dumb. And I'm not dumb either. The truth is, you are partly right. Neither of us is a genius, but we aren't stupid either, that's for sure. I'm not bragging, but tell me — isn't it true that until the middle of fifth grade I was considered even worse than you?"

"Well," answered Hillel, "not really worse than me, but you weren't a good student."

"Fine," said Motti. "So listen: I once thought the way you do — that I wasn't a good student and there was nothing I could do about it. But then I decided that even if I'm not so smart, I can at least work hard and be average. And isn't it true that I've gotten better?

"Yes, you have," admitted Hillel.

"That's what I wanted to hear. So if you make up your mind that you can do it, you'll be able to do it."

With that Motti concluded the argument and went back to explaining the Gemara.

*       *       *

While Motti and Hillel were arguing, Reb Daniel, Hillel's father, walked into the cheder. He wanted to talk to the rebbe. Because the pupils were

*While Motti and Hillel were arguing, Hillel's father spoke to the rebbe privately.*

busy reviewing the Gemara lesson with their chavrusas, as we have already mentioned, the rebbe was able to stand by the door of the classroom and speak privately with Hillel's father while glancing at the boys in the classroom from time to time.

"Hillel does not pay attention as he should," said the rebbe. "It seems as if he has given up and is no longer concerned about his low grades." The rebbe told Hillel's father that he had suggested to Hillel that he make a special effort to pay attention, and that every week that he paid attention as he should, he would get a prize. But Hillel never made the special effort.

Reb Daniel sighed and asked the rebbe, "Maybe my son really is a poor student. Maybe it really is hard for him to learn, maybe he isn't capable of learning."

"I assure you, he is capable," said the rebbe, " but he has given up on himself."

Reb Daniel thanked the rebbe, called to Hillel, asked him to try harder, and left the cheder feeling depressed and sad.

Reb Daniel was still close to the cheder when whom should he see walking toward him on the opposite side of the street but Reb Aryeh, Motti's father. Something stirred inside him and he called out, "Reb Aryeh, Reb Aryeh, please wait up!"

Reb Aryeh paused and Reb Daniel crossed to where he was standing. "Please forgive me, Reb Aryeh," said Reb Daniel, "but do you have a minute or two for me? I want to ask you something."

Reb Aryeh said, "I'm all ears."

"Please, Reb Aryeh," said Reb Daniel, "please help me. I mean, help me with my son Hillel."

"What's the matter? And how can I help you?" said Reb Aryeh in surprise.

"I'll tell you," said Reb Daniel. "Who knows better than you how until two years ago our precious sons were both weak students? I remember the times we talked about it and how you said that we, the parents, have to pray. Who knows better than I how unhappy you were to see your son's difficulties in cheder?"

"What you say is true," said Reb Aryeh.

"And so, Reb Aryeh, think about what has happened. Both boys had trouble understanding the material. Neither participated in the lessons, and both got low grades. But all of a sudden your Motti begins to grow and flourish while my Hillel is still stuck in the mud. Don't misunderstand me! I am not, chas v'shalom, unhappy that your son is doing well in cheder. On the contrary! It makes me very happy to hear that your Motti now wants to learn and is making progress, not only because you are my friend, but because it gives me hope that just as your son went from darkness to light, maybe… maybe… " Reb Daniel sighed. "Maybe my son will also start doing better," he said, and his eyes filled with tears.

Reb Daniel continued. "You are probably wondering why I stopped you. This is why: Please tell me what you did. How did this amazing change happen? How did your son's brain suddenly open up? I am sure you had something to do with it. Please tell me: Did you fast? Read all of Sefer Tehillim every day? Pray at the Kosel forty days without a break?"

"I'm truly sorry," answered Reb Aryeh. "I'm not on such a high level, to fast or to read all of Tehillim every day. Of course I prayed that my son would do well, but I am sure that you do, too."

"Oh! How much my wife and I pray!" exclaimed Reb Daniel. "But maybe you found an avreich who was both sharp and tactful and who succeeded in bringing out your son's ability. After all, it's simply a miracle."

"No, Reb Daniel," said Reb Aryeh. "My son Motti did not miraculously develop new abilities overnight. The change in him took a long time and a lot of hard work. And the process continues even now."

"But Reb Aryeh, my son also wants very much to learn Torah, but he doesn't succeed. It broke my heart when two weeks ago he said to me that he is stupid and there is no hope for him. Why doesn't my son succeed in his efforts like yours?"

Reb Aryeh was silent. He knew of no way to console the distraught father, and he didn't want to criticize him. But he knew Hillel's future might depend on his parents' attitude toward him and his studies. Therefore, he stirred himself and said to Reb Daniel, "It may be that I have some explanation for my son's improvement, and also a good idea for you. Tell me, when your son comes home from cheder with a test on which is displayed the grade 'fifty,' what do you do?"

"Nu, what can I do?" answered Reb Daniel. "It's not the boy's fault, so it goes without saying that I don't yell at him, but nevertheless I ask him to sit down next to me, and I explain to him that he could have gotten a higher grade if he had paid attention a little more, and… that's it."

"Does your son notice that you are upset by his getting a low grade?" asked Reb Aryeh, continuing to probe.

"And how he knows! I know that it hurts him to see me upset because of him."

"Well," said Reb Aryeh carefully, "the truth is that you might be interfering with your child's ability to succeed."

"I?" cried Reb Daniel. "I don't understand. Was there something wrong with the reaction I described to you?"

"There was. It was a mistake to react that way," exclaimed Reb Aryeh. "Let me tell you what I myself did when my son came home with a test with a grade of fifty." Then, as Reb Daniel stood with his eyes wide in astonishment, Reb Aryeh described the scene vividly:

"Shalom, Motti! I see that you have brought a test for me to sign. You got fifty? That's good! It means you know five correct answers. Take yourself a sweet from the pantry."

"Abba, you're making fun of me," said Motti.

"I am not," I said seriously. "Imagine that someone came to me and asked me ten difficult riddles, and that I succeeded in answering four of them. I assure you that I would be very proud of myself, because, after all, I answered four difficult riddles. And you, my dear Motti, know that the questions on Gemara tests are often really complicated, like a difficult riddle, and still you knew five complete answers, which means that you understand the material very well."

"Were you pretending?" asked Reb Daniel in surprise.

"At the start, it was just an act meant to encourage my son," answered Reb Aryeh, "but after a time, when I had made my son believe how wonderful it was that he could answer five questions correctly, I began to honestly believe that this was a significant accomplishment."

"And then what happened? How did this help your Motti?" asked Reb Daniel, his interest awakening.

"The moment that Motti felt I was truly happy about his test grades, he himself began to be happy about knowing five correct answers. And no doubt he thought, 'So I do understand! Abba is right.' And seeing how happy I was and being convinced that he did understand, Motti tried a little harder and… lo and behold! he came home one day holding a test, and on it was displayed the grade 'sixty-five.'"

"And then?" asked Reb Daniel expectantly.

"And then there was real jubilation in the house. 'Did you hear, Imma? Our Motti was asked ten questions and knew everything except three and a half answers. Motti, run to the grocery store and buy yourself an ice cream.' Motti began to flourish the moment he realized that even if he understood just one line on a page of Gemara, that was an accomplishment."

"How do you know that this is the reason for his becoming a good student?" asked Reb Daniel.

"He himself told me so," answered Reb Aryeh.

"Are you sure that my doing as you suggest will help Hillel improve as a student? asked Reb Daniel.

"I am almost certain of it," answered Reb Aryeh, "but you have to work on yourself. I mean, you truly have to be happy with your son's 'fifty.' And why shouldn't you be? Hillel doesn't neglect his studies. He studies and he learns. He knows at least half of what was taught."

"Yes, but the other boys in the class know it all," said Reb Daniel.

"What does it matter to you what the other boys know? Tell me, would you be happy if your son knew half of Shas by heart?"

"Half of Shas by heart? What kind of a question is that? Of course I would be happy," replied Reb Daniel.

"Would you be happy even if you learned that your son's classmates knew the whole Shas by heart, and not just half of it?"

"Even then I would be happy. After all, to know half the Shas is a tremendous thing, even if others know it all."

"So," said Reb Aryeh, "your son knows half a page of Gemara. Be happy. As soon as you are happy, your Hillel will be happy. And when he is happy, he will realize that he can understand the lessons. And when he realizes that he can understand, he will begin to do better."

Reb Daniel was so moved by Reb Aryeh's words that he hugged him. "You are a true educator!" he exclaimed. "How did you figure out that one must be happy about even a little Torah?"

"I learned it from your son Hillel," replied Reb Aryeh.

"You learned it from Hillel? What do you mean?" asked Reb Daniel in surprise.

"It was about two years ago," said Reb Aryeh, "when the boys were playing that game with apricot pits. As I was leaving our building with my son Yitzi, who was about five at the time, I passed Hillel and some of his friends playing in the lobby, trying to toss the apricot pits through a hole in the top of a can.

"As we passed the boys, Yitzi said he wanted to try, but he didn't have any apricot pits. Hillel gave him a present of ten pits, and Yitzi tried, but didn't get even one pit into the can. He wailed that he didn't know how to do it.

*"Your Hillel took pity on him and gave him another ten pits — but first he moved the can closer to where Yitzi was standing and took the top off. This time, Yitzi managed to get three of the ten pits into the can, and Hillel told him that he had done very well, that he was just like a big boy, getting three into the can.*

*"That evening my wife showed me a test Motti had brought home that day on which he had gotten only three answers right. I looked at the test — sadly, I don't have to tell you — but then I heard in my mind the words Hillel had spoken to Yitzi earlier: 'Very good, Yitzi! You're a big boy! You hit the target three times!' Then it was as if I heard an echo: 'Three times! Three times! Three times…' It was then that I really understood that in order to get four, you first have to be happy that you can get three, and that you cannot aim for five until you have mastered four and are happy with it. I learned this lesson from Hillel. When I think about this, I really think that Hillel deserves to have someone say to him, 'Very good! You know five correct answers.'"*

Rebbe Mendel finished and said, "That's it. That's the end of the story as I heard it from Hillel's father. Reb Daniel took Reb Aryeh's advice and was surprised at the change for the better in his son's schoolwork. Ever since I heard this story I write, "Wrote five correct answers' instead of 'fifty,' and hope that next time, with Hashem's help, the pupil will be able to answer at least six questions correctly.

"And while we're on the subject, I want to tell you that you should be happy about every good thing you do, no matter how small it seems to you — every *berachah* you say with *kavanah*, every time you participate in the *shiur*. Being happy about your small successes will bring more and more of them."

# GLOSSARY

The following glossary provides a partial explanation of some of the Hebrew, Yiddish (Y.) and Aramaic (A.) words and phrases used in this book. The spellings and explanations reflect the way the specific word is used herein. Often, there are alternate spellings and meanings for the words.

AGGADOS: Jewish teachings, forming especially the non-halachic parts of the TALMUD.

AGMAS NEFESH: distress, anguish.

AL KIDDUSH HASHEM: for the sanctification of God's Name.

AM YISRAEL: the People of Israel, that is, the Jewish People.

ANI MA'AMIN: a popular song culled from Rambam's Thirteen Principles of Faith, referring to the belief in the coming of the Messiah.

ARON BRIS HASHEM: the "ark of the covenant"; the Holy Ark in the *Mishkan* and the BEIS HAMIKDASH.

ASHREI: the introduction to the MINCHAH prayer, composed mainly of TEHILLIM 145.

AVRAHAM AVINU: Abraham our (fore)father.

AVREICH: a young married man (usually in KOLLEL).

BA'AL TESHUVAH: a formerly non-observant Jew who becomes religiously observant.

BA'ALEI HA-TOSAFOS: a school of about eighty French and German Torah scholars from the twelfth and thirteenth centuries who wrote commentaries on the talmud.

BACHUR (PL. BACHURIM): YESHIVA student(s).

201

BARUCH HA-BA: "Welcome!"

BARUCH HASHEM: "Thank God!"

BARUCH MECHAYEH HA-MEISIM: a blessing recited upon seeing someone after a long time.

BEDIKAS CHAMETZ: the search for CHAMETZ conducted on the night before Pesach.

BEIN HA-ZEMANIM: intersession break in YESHIVAS.

BEIS HAMIKDASH: the Holy Temple in Jerusalem.

BEIS MIDRASH: a Torah study hall.

BEKIYUS: erudition.

BEMIDBAR: the Book of Numbers.

BERACHAH (PL. BERACHOS): a blessing.

BEREISHIS: the Book of Genesis.

B'EZRAS HASHEM: "With God's help."

BITTUL TORAH: wasting time from studying Torah.

B'LI NEDER: a phrase that changes a firm promise into an intention.

BRIS: the circumcision ceremony.

CHALILAH: "God forbid!"

CHAMETZ: leavened food, prohibited during Passover.

CHAREIDI: lit., "[God-]fearing"; sometimes used derogatorily by secular Jews and others to describe "ultra-Orthodox" Jews.

CHAS V'SHALOM: "God forbid!"

CHAVRUSA: (A.) a Torah study partner.

CHAZAL: a Hebrew acronym for "Our Sages of blessed memory."

CHEDER: (Y.) a Jewish primary school for boys.

CHESHBON HANEFESH: moral stock-taking; introspection.

CHILLUL HASHEM: the desecration of God's Name.

CHODESH TOV: "A good month!"; the greeting given to a fellow Jew on ROSH CHODESH.

CHOZER/CHOZRIM B'TESHUVAH: see BA'AL TESHUVAH, above.

DAF YOMI: the program for learning one folio page of TALMUD each day.

DAVEN: (Y.) pray.

DERASHAH: Torah discourse(s).

DIN TORAH: a dispute judged by a rabbinical court or judge in accordance with Jewish law.

DIN: law.

DIVREI MUSSAR: words of Torah ethics and values.

DIVREI TORAH: short presentations of Torah thoughts.

EISHES CHAYIL: a "woman of valor," from Proverbs 31.

ELIYAHU HA-NAVI: Elijah the Prophet.

FRUM: (Y.) religious.

GABBAI: the secretary or treasurer of a synagogue.

GALUS: exile.

GAN EDEN: literally, the Garden of Eden; Paradise.

GAON/GEONIM: a genius in Torah learning.

GEDOLEI HA-DOR: great Torah sages and leaders of the generation.

GEMARA: (A.) commentary of the MISHNAH (together they comprise the TALMUD); a volume of the TALMUD.

GESHMAK: (Y.) lit., "tasty"; spiritually pleasurable.

GOY: a non-Jew.

HACHNASAS KALLAH: the mitzvah of providing for a poor bride's needs.

HAFTARAH: a passage from NEVI'IM, read after the Torah reading in the synagogue on Shabbos.

HA-KADOSH BARUCH HU: the Holy One, Blessed is He, i.e., God.

HALACHAH (PL. HALACHOS): Jewish law.

HASHEM YISBARACH: Hashem, may He be blessed.

HASHEM: God.

HASHGACHAH PRATIS: Divine Providence.

HISORERUS: spiritual awakening.

IMMA: mother, mommy.

IYAR: the Hebrew month corresponding to April-May.

KADDISH: the mourner's prayer, sanctifying God's Name.

KAPPARAH: atonement.

KASHRUS: the Jewish dietary laws.

KAVANAH: concentration.

KAYIN: Adam's son Cain.

KIDDUSH HASHEM: the sanctification of God's Name; behavior
that raises public appreciation of HASHEM.

KIDDUSH SHEM SHAMAYIM: see KIDDUSH HASHEM, above.

KIN'AS SOFERIM: a competitive envy of and admiration for another person's knowledge that spurs on more study.

KIPPAH: skullcap, yarmulke.

KOHELES: the Book of Ecclesiastes.

KOLLEL: a center for advanced Torah study for adult students,
mostly married men.

KOSEL: the Western Wall of the Temple Mount in Jerusalem.

LAG BA-OMER: the thirty-third of the forty-nine days of the
counting of the Omer, a joyful day interrupting a period of
semi-mourning.

LAMDAN: a Torah scholar possessing an in-depth knowledge of
the Talmud.

LAMDUS: erudition.

LASHON HA-RA: gossip; speaking badly about another person.

LEVI (PL. LEVIYIM): a Levite; a member of the tribe of Levi.

L'HAVDIL: "to differentiate," a phrase used when mentioning
holy and unholy matters together.

MA'ARIV: the evening prayer service.

MA'ASER: tithes on produce.

MAGGID SHIUR: the lecturer who gives a SHIUR.

MAGGID: a preacher.

MASECHES: a Mishnaic or Talmudic tractate.

MASHIACH: the Messiah.

MAZAL TOV: "Congratulations!"

MECHALLEL SHEM SHAMAYIM: to desecrate the Name of God.

MIDDOS: character traits; qualities or attributes.

MIDRASH: non-literal or non-legal interpretations or homiletic teachings of the Sages.

MINCHAH: the afternoon prayer service.

MINYAN: a quorum of ten men needed for a public prayer service.

MISHKAN: the Tabernacle in the desert — the precursor to the BEIS HAMIKDASH.

MISHNAH (PL. MISHNAYOS): the codified Oral Law redacted by Rabbi Yehudah HaNasi; a specific paragraph of the Oral Law.

MITZVAH: a commandment; a good deed.

MOSHAV: an agricultural settlement.

MUSSAR: Torah ethics and values aimed at character improvement.

NACHAS: pleasure, satisfaction.

NESHAMOS: souls.

NEVI'IM: lit., "Prophets"; the second division of the TANACH, which consists of books written by the prophets.

NU: (Y.) "Well?" or "So?"

PARASHAH: the weekly Torah portion.

PELISHTIM: the Philistines.

PESHAT: the simple meaning; an explanation.

PEYOS: sidelocks.

PIKUACH NEFESH: saving an endangered life or lives.

PIRKEI AVOS: *Ethics of the Fathers,* a tractate of the MISHNAH.

POSEK (PL. POSKIM): an authority on Jewish law.

RABBEINU: our teacher.

RAV: a rabbi.

REBBE: a Torah teacher.

RIBBONO SHEL OLAM: Master of the Universe, i.e., God.

RISHONIM: the classic Torah scholars who lived between the eras of the TALMUD and the *Shulchan Aruch*.

ROSH CHODESH: the first day of the Hebrew month.

ROSH YESHIVA: the dean of a yeshiva.

RUACH HA-KODESH: lit, "the holy spirit"; a lower degree of prophecy; Divine inspiration.

SANDEK: (Y.) the person who has the honor of holding the baby at his BRIS.

SEFER TEHILLIM: the book of Psalms.

SEFER: a book; a holy book.

SEFIRAS HAOMER: the seven-week period of the counting of the Omer, between the festivals of Passover and Shavuos.

SHACHARIS: the morning prayer service.

SHALOM ALEICHEM: "May peace be with you," a traditional Jewish greeting.

SHAS: a Hebrew acronym for the entire Talmud.

SHAVUOS: lit., "weeks," the festival celebrated seven weeks after Passover, when firstfruits may begin to be brought to the BEIS HAMIKDASH.

SHECHINAH: the Divine Presence of God.

SHECHITAH: ritual slaughter.

SHEMUEL: the Book of Samuel.

SHINUI: a change.

SHIR HASHIRIM: the Song of Songs.

SHIUR (PL. SHIURIM): Torah class(es).

SHLITA: a Hebrew acronym for "May he live long."

SHMUZE: (Y.) a talk with a moral lesson.

SHOCHET (PL. SHOCHTIM): a ritual slaughterer.

SHOMER MITZVOS: one who observe the MITZVOS.

SHTENDER: (Y.) a stand or lectern used for prayer or individual study.

SHUL: (Y.) a synagogue.

SIVAN: the Hebrew month corresponding to May-June.

SUGYA: (A.) a topic, particularly give-and-take argumentation in the Gemara.

SVARA/SVAROS: (A.) logical reasoning.

TALMID CHACHAM: a Torah scholar.

TALMID(IM): student(s) [of Torah].

TALMUD TORAH: a Jewish elementary school for boys.

TALMUD: the basic corpus of Jewish law (200 B.C.E.–500 C.E.), consisting of the MISHNAH and GEMARA.

TANACH: a Hebrew acronym for the entire Bible.

TE'AMIM: cantillation used when reciting the Torah.

TEFILLAH: prayer.

TEFILLIN: small leather boxes encasing specific Torah verses written on parchment and worn by men during weekday morning prayers.

TEHILLIM: the Book of Psalms.

TERUMAH: tithes on produce.

TISHAH B'AV: the ninth day of the Hebrew month of Av, which is a national Jewish mourning day.

TORANI: serious commitment to Torah.

TOSAFOS: an early commentary on the TALMUD.

TU B'AV: the fifteenth day of the Hebrew month of Av, considered a minor holiday.

TZADDIK: a righteous person.

TZEDAKAH: charity.

TZEFAS: the city of Safed.

VILNA GAON: the "genius of Vilna," i.e., Rabbi Eliyahu (Kramer) of Vilna (1720–1797).

VORT: (Y.) lit., "word"; a short Torah thought or discourse.

YASHAR KOACH: "Good for you!"

YEHAREG V'AL YA'AVOR: instances where one must forfeit his life rather than transgress a Torah commandment.

YERUSHALAYIM: Jerusalem.

YESHAYAHU: the Book of Isaiah.

YESHIVA GEDOLAH: a post-high school YESHIVA.

YESHIVA: an academy of Torah study.

YETZER HA-RA: the evil inclination.

YIDDISHKEIT: (Y.) Judaism.

YINGELEH: (Y.) a little boy.

YIRAS SHAMAYIM: fear of Heaven.

YOSEF HA-TZADDIK: "Joseph the righteous" (see BEREISHIS 41:39–45).